Contents

D0489504

Contents

Contents

Contents

Contents

Central heating wet – 1

Scope

Information contained in this Part provides guidance for the installation, service and maintenance of central heating boilers, combination boilers, condensing boilers and combined gas fire/back boiler/back circulators that are 'CE' or British Standard (BS) kite marked. The information may also be referred to for used or second-hand appliances not carrying the CE or BS kite-mark but with a data plate bearing information ensuring that the appliance is suitable for the gas type and pressure. I.e. Natural gas at an appliance inlet pressure of 20mbar and Liquefied Petroleum Gas (LPG) Propane and Butane where the supply regulator has been set to provide an operating pressure of 37mbar and 28mbar respectively.

Note: Information in this Part should also be read in conjunction with the relevant part(s) of the Gas Installer Manual Series – Essential Gas Safety – Domestic.

Introduction

No person shall carry out any work (see **Part 13 Definitions**) in relation to gas appliances and other gas fittings or gas storage vessels covered by this manual unless they are competent to do so.

When any work is carried out, gas installing businesses must be registered and their gas operatives must hold a valid certificate of competence for each work activity that they wish to undertake. The certificate must have been issued under the Nationally Accredited Certification Scheme (ACS) for individual gas fitting operatives.

No employer, member of the public or other responsible person should knowingly employ a gas operative who cannot comply with the above requirements.

All gas appliances and other gas fittings must be installed in accordance with the Gas Safety (Installation and Use) Regulations, British Standards, Building Regulations, Regulations for Electrical Installations or those Regulations appropriate to the geographical region in which they are to be installed. Due regard needs to be given to the manufacturer's installation instructions.

Information contained in this manual has been developed after gathering data and information from various sources, which CORGI believes, reflects current custom and practice within the sector.

The heating system

Background

Gas central heating boilers covered in this manual can generally trace their origins back to high thermal capacity (water content) cast iron floor-mounted solid fuel boilers, where hot water circulation around the circuit was instigated by gravity, i.e. a differential in density between hot water flow (lighter) and cool water return (heavier).

Gravity circulation was generally via large capacity single cast iron/steel pipe circuits, installed on the internal perimeter walls of a building. Heating the building relied on the pipework acting as a heat emitter.

High thermal capacity radiators were introduced later, but the principle of circulation remained the same – gravity circulation. It was important for circulation, that the pipework was correctly designed and installed with either a rise from or fall back to the boiler. Even then, water circulation was fairly slow. Due to the pipe sizes involved and the costs of installation, it is not surprising that central heating was generally confined to factories, churches and large country houses.

Temperature control of the hot water storage vessel (cylinder) was generally achieved by use of the boiler thermostat. However a refinement of this basic control method was by the fitting of a manually adjustable thermostatic control valve in the return pipework from the storage vessel. However, due to lack of maintenance these valves often seized in the closed or semi-closed position, which results in poor circulation. Alternatively, an electrically operated valve (controlled by a cylinder thermostat) may have been fitted in the flow or return pipework to the storage vessel.

A change for the better

In the 1960s gas central heating was introduced into the domestic market. The boilers at this time were predominantly of the floor standing, cast iron types, but they still retained the high thermal capacity (13-14 litres water content) derivatives of solid fuel boilers. An accelerator (circulating pump) introduced into the small-bore central heating pipework system did however improve circulation to radiators. Circulation was quite often via a small-bore (15mm equivalent size) copper single pipe system.

Water circulation to the domestic hot water storage vessel continued to be driven by gravity. An innovative back boiler was also introduced at about this time but even this appliance retained the option of gravity circulation to the storage vessel.

Feed and expansion cistern

The systems main safety feature was another solid fuel method/practice where, in the event of a boiler thermostat failure, water would boil, expand, and discharge through an open vent pipe into the feed and expansion cistern before returning to the boiler via a cold feed supply pipe. This cycle would continue until the user's attention was attracted by the noise generated by the boiling water, whereupon the system could be hastily shut down.

Single pipe systems

Single pipe systems are no longer installed, however many still exist. Some of the problems associated with them and the methods of upgrading such systems are included here.

A single pipe system is a simple ring circuit. A central heating system may consist of one circuit serving the whole house (see Figure 1.1) or it may have multiple circuits (see Figure 1.2), with each circuit serving an individual part of a dwelling. For example, a three bedroom semi-detached property may have two circuits, one serving the upstairs radiators, the other serving the downstairs radiators.

Although the main circulation through the pipework is pumped, the water circulates through the radiators mainly by gravity. However, because the water is pumped around the circuit there will be a gradual pressure loss between the circulating pump outlet and inlet. Consequently, there is a differential in pressure between the tee pieces serving each radiator. This pressure differential also assists circulation to each radiator.

Because circulation to each radiator was by gravity, it was essential that the pipe circuit was installed close to the radiator, with the radiator inlet and outlet connecting pipe tee pieces installed close to the radiator valves. Failure to observe this rule often resulted in either poor circulation or even no circulation at all through the radiator. As stated, circulation to a radiator is dependent on gravity circulation and a slight differential in water pressure between the inlet and outlet connections of the radiator. It follows, therefore, that the greater the distance between the tee pieces, the greater the differential in pressure will be, assisting the flow through the radiator.

It is clear, then, that there was little force available to aid circulation to a radiator on a single pipe system. Care should therefore be taken, when re-siting radiators to redirect the main pipe circuit so that it is redirected as close as possible to the new radiator position. Failure to observe this rule will almost certainly result in poor circulation or no circulation to the radiator.

In single pipe systems the domestic hot water storage vessel flow and return pipework often relies on gravity circulation only (see **Hot water storage vessels** in this Part).

As well as a loss of pressure through the system pipework, allowances have to be made for the loss of temperature through the system. Water flowing through each radiator loses heat into the room before subsequently flowing back into the same system pipework and onto the next radiator. This has the effect of reducing the water temperature to the next and subsequent radiator(s) on the system. Allowances therefore need to be made for this by sizing each radiator based on the projected water flow temperature available to the radiators on a single pipe system. This will in most cases mean larger radiators.

Upgrading single pipe systems with thermostatic radiator valves (TRV)

It is important when upgrading this type of system with thermostatic radiator valves that only valves suitable for a single-pipe system are used.

TRVs designed for fully pumped systems are unsuitable because the reduced valve area creates a high resistance to water flow, which will often prevent circulation or certainly reduce it.

Another problem encountered, is the mistake of fitting thermostatic radiator valves to the bottom radiator connections. Warm convection air currents from the hot main central heating circuit below the radiator often cause premature closure of the valve, with the valve remaining closed during the heating period. Mysteriously, the 'fault' corrects itself on initial start-up of the system (with everything cool) but followed shortly afterwards by heat from the main central heating circuit causing premature closure again.

Figure 1.1 Single pipe ring circuit

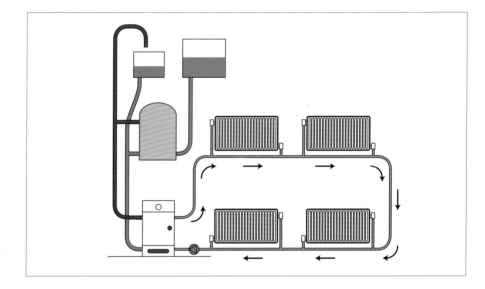

Figure 1.2 Single pipe circuit with two ring circuits

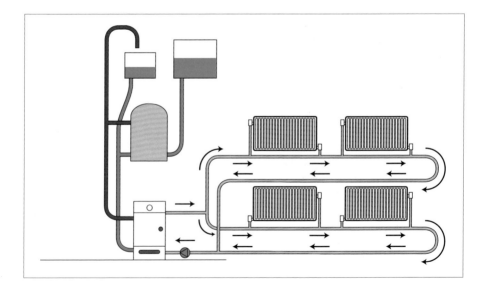

Figure 1.3 A basic two pipe central heating system

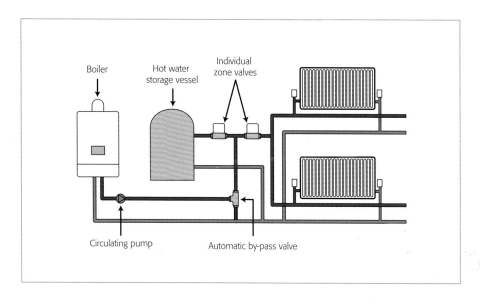

Two pipe systems

Early two pipe systems were generally a refinement of single pipe systems, which still relied on gravity fed hot water to the hot water storage vessel.

Modern systems will almost certainly be designed around a two-pipe system, heating all rooms simultaneously to full comfort temperatures see Figure 1.3 (see also **Comfort conditions** in this Part).

The system will almost certainly incorporate a programmer to control heating times and thermostats to control the temperatures of both domestic hot water and central heating. The system will be fully pumped with individual flow and return pipes to each radiator. The boiler may be either floor-standing, wall-mounted or a fire/back boiler serving the needs of both heating and hot water demands.

Alternatively, a combination boiler may be installed serving the needs of both the heating and hot water in a combined unit. Combination boilers are normally installed onto 'sealed systems' (see **Part 4 Combination boilers – Sealed system** for further guidance). Combination boiler are also available to operate in the condensing 'mode' (see **Part 5 Condensing boilers** for further guidance).

Most systems continue to be installed with the traditional separate open vent pipe that is discharging over a feed and expansion cistern, sited at the highest point in the installation, e.g. the roof space.

The cistern will be supplied with water from the cold water main and have a separate cold feed supplying water to the circulating pipework. It is essential that no valve is fitted to the cold feed pipe which may if closed prevent expansion of the water during the heating period.

Most modern boilers, however, are equipped with an integral overheat thermostat. Alternatively, the overheat thermostat may be available as an optional extra from the boiler manufacturer. The overheat thermostat is generally set to operate at a temperature of 95°C to prevent the system water from boiling.

In some circumstances, a combined cold feed/open vent arrangement can be installed especially in the case of a low head installation. This is where the boiler is sited 'high up' in the building generally less than 1m head (the level of the water in the feed and expansion tank above the boiler). In such cases where the appliance incorporates an overheat thermostat and manufacturer's instructions allow, the open vent and cold feed may be combined in a single pipe. In this case, there is no necessity for the system to have a separate open vent, only a suitably sized cold feed and expansion cistern to accommodate the hot expanded water.

When this method is used, the boiler manufacturer's instructions will often stipulate that the combined cold feed and open vent pipe should not be less than 20mm in internal diameter. There should be no valves or components other than full-bore pipe fittings between the boiler and the feed and expansion cistern.

Boilers fitted with this overheat cut-off device are often used as a 'package' with other controls on sealed systems.

Heating and hot water

Whilst boilers have been reduced in size and thermal capacity, radiators and hot water storage vessels have also gone through a period of change. Boilers these days will almost certainly be serving smaller thermal capacity radiators and a fully pumped fast recovery hot water storage vessels. The storage vessel may be remote from the boiler, or it may be combined with the boiler within the boiler case.

The following information on the design of wet central heating systems is provided as general guidance only. Due to the varying complexities and requirements of correct design, CORGI Services Limited have produced a publication, Wet Central Heating System Design Guide which is intended to serve as a working guide for those who design wet central heating systems.

This publication is available from CORGIdirect, quoting order ref: WCH1 on Tel: 0800 915 0490 or online at www.corgi-direct.com

Hot water storage vessels

If a customer wishes to retain a system with gravity circulation to the storage vessel, most modern boiler manufacturers can provide boilers that will satisfy existing system requirements. It is questionable, however, whether heat recovery by this method is fast enough to satisfy current or future customer expectations.

Using a 15kW output boiler and standard hot water storage vessel (900mm x 450mm), gravity circulation can take up to 90 minutes to heat the water. This figure will vary depending on how good or bad circulation is to the vessel.

In contrast, a standard hot water storage vessel with pumped primaries will deliver approximately 175 litres of hot water in 40 minutes. A fast recovery vessel will deliver 340 litres of hot water in the same 40 minute period and of course, take up significantly less space in the airing cupboard.

Fast recovery storage vessel

A modern, fully pumped fast recovery hot water storage vessel, incorporating a multi-strand heat exchanger and serving the average 3 bedroom semi-detached household, is likely to have a storage capacity of 45 litres, stand 600mm high and have a diameter of 350mm. This is considerably smaller than the average gravity-fed hot water storage vessel of yesteryear. Provided an appropriate boiler and controls are fitted, recovery times for these modern vessels are typically 8 minutes from cold from a 15kW output boiler. This size of vessel is ideally suited for use by those families who prefer to shower, however they are also quite capable of supplying a standard length (1700mm) bath. 60 litre and larger options are available for the larger than average household or where there is an exceptional demand for hot water.

Comfort conditions

The human body is probably at its most comfortable when it is doing the least amount of work. A healthy body should maintain its temperature at a steady 36.9°C.

If the body starts to get cold, the pores close and shivering produces rapid movement in an endeavour to raise the body temperature to normal. On the other hand, when the body becomes too hot, the pores open and sweating occurs. As the moisture evaporates, it takes heat from the body and lowers the body temperature.

The body is comfortable when, during any activity, the heat it is producing exactly matches the amount of heat being lost. When the body does not have any work to do its temperature is kept steady.

To give a feeling of freshness there needs to be air movement in a room. Excessive movement or draughts make us feel cold even when the air temperature is still quite high. In summer, a fan can be used to help us keep cool although it does not actually reduce air temperature.

What it does do is help to increase the rate at which perspiration is being evaporated, thus increasing the rate at which heat is taken from the body.

Having established the basic requirements for comfort conditions the next step is to reproduce the conditions in a dwelling. The following criteria will help create these.

Full central heating should be designed to maintain comfort conditions with an outside temperature of -1°C.

However, to reach and maintain the temperatures in Table 1.1 when the outside temperature is -1°C or less, it may be necessary to set the boiler thermostat control to its maximum setting and override the heating time controls. This would include, setting programmers to 24-hour operation and setting room or radiator thermostats to their maximum settings.

Similarly, during a cold period, if a system has been off overnight or during the day, rooms will be unable to reach the temperatures indicated in Table 1.1 within a short period of turning on the heating system, unless an additional heat source is available in that room, e.g. a gas fire.

The fabric of a building or room left unheated will cool. Consequently, it will absorb most of the heat being produced once the heating system is turned on which may take several hours in traditional built dwellings.

BS EN 12828 Heating systems in buildings – Design for water-based heating systems, recommends that 'comfortable' temperatures for activities and air changes in a dwelling should be as shown in Table 1.1.

Table 1.1 Temperature and air changes on which heat loss calculations should be based

Room	Room Temperature °C*	Air Changes per hour‡
Living room	21	1.5
Dining room	21	1.5
Bedsitting room	21	1.5
Bedroom†	18	1
Hall/Landing	18	1.5
Bathroom	22	2
Kitchen	18	2
Toilet	18	2

* These are the temperatures recommended for whole house central heating and for individual rooms with part central heating. Where open-flue appliances are installed the number of air changes should be increased.

‡ Note: Figures in this Table are based on individual rooms that are isolated from each other e.g. with interconnecting doors closed and with the air changes so described. A room that contains a solid fuel chimney and fire grate that is open to the room may be subject to a greater number of air changes – especially if the solid fuel fire or decorative fuel effect gas appliance is alight – in which case it may be difficult to reach the desired temperatures indicated in this Table.

† When bedrooms are used as bedsitting rooms, or for studying purposes, a higher temperature may be required.

Building Regulations (England and Wales) Approved Document 'L' (ADL)

The building regulations for England and Wales are closely linked with SAP (the Government's Standard Assessment Procedure for Energy Rating of Dwellings), SEDBUK (Seasonal Efficiency of Domestic Boilers in the UK) and CHeSS 2005 (Central heating system specifications).

ADL effects the conservation of fuel and power in all types of buildings and sets out requirements for dwellings and other buildings, outlining construction techniques, lighting, insulation and heating, to promote the most economic use of fossil fuels.

There are four main aspects to ADL. It is necessary to reduce heat escaping from the fabric of the building. Roofs, walls, windows, doors and floors should have an adequate resistance to heat loss. Hot water pipes, hot air ducts and hot water vessels should also limit any heat loss.

Space heating and hot water systems need to be energy efficient and adequate controls should be provided to control appliances/heating and hot water systems to avoid inefficient usage and waste. To ensure this, customers should be provided with appropriate information to help them operate and maintain heating and hot water systems economically.

A major revamp of the Building Regulations has been necessary due to buildings contributing to a high proportion of the carbon dioxide (CO_2) emissions and the government's targets of reducing CO_2 levels.

For compliance in dwellings, various energy efficiency-rating methods are used to demonstrate that a reasonable provision has been made for the conservation of fuel. It is now necessary for both new and modified dwellings that are within the regulations, to be subjected to an Energy Rating, i.e. SAP. The SAP rating scale is from 1-100, where 1 denotes a very poor standard of energy efficiency and 100 is exceptionally high.

Compliance with SAP may be achieved by combining a number of energy conservation methods. The regulations however also contain stringent provisions regarding central heating appliances.

The performance standards in ADL are significantly higher than those introduced in 1995 and this may have an impact on the selection and the installation of domestic and non domestic appliances and plant. Within the requirements, consideration is made for a reasonable provision for appliance efficiency; this may be established by utilising an appliance with a minimum SEDBUK rating.

Building work under ADL

Under the regulations building work must be pre notified to an appropriate Building Control Body, however if the business is a member of a competent persons scheme the work is notified to the provider after completion they in turn notify the relevant building control department.

Where the installation of a gas appliance is concerned, the amendment to the Building Regulations stipulates that where the person is competent, as defined in the regulations, it is not necessary to notify Building Control prior to carrying out the work.

Definition of competence (Building Regulations)

In order to meet the requirements of the Building Regulations the installer of a gas appliance or fitting, including the installation of chimney, must be competent. Under the Gas Safety (Installation and Use) Regulations (GSIUR) a registered gas operative, with current certificates in the relevant ACS modules, or a valid equivalent, is deemed competent. This same definition is used to define competency for the purposes of the Building Regulations.

A registered gas operative is therefore deemed competent for other building work necessary for the installation of the appliance, such as the installation of a chimney, although there are some exceptions.

Seasonal Efficiency of Domestic Boilers in the United Kingdom (SEDBUK)

SEDBUK ratings classify appliances for their average efficiency in terms of fuel consumed in return for heat produced and are designed to offer a true comparison as to relative efficiency. The rating is calculated considering the boiler type, ignition, the UK climate and fuel usage patterns, as well as standard laboratory tests.

Wet gas central heating appliances (boilers) installed in newly constructed buildings and buildings that have been refurbished should have a SEDBUK gross efficiency rating of 78% for Natural gas appliances and 80% for Liquefied Petroleum Gas (LPG) appliances (see the manuals Wet Central Heating System Design Guide or the Domestic Heating Compliance Guide for further guidance. See **Part 14 CORGI Services Limited Publications**).

The necessary controls will need to support the appliance to allow the full SEDBUK performance to be achieved. Temperature controls are necessary for the dwelling and provisions are also made for the 'heat exchange' efficiency and adequate insulation for domestic hot water storage vessels. It may be necessary for hot water pipework and hot air ducts to be provided with adequate insulation.

When undertaking refurbishment work, it is recommended that gravity hot water systems are upgraded to a fully pumped design with adequate temperature control added.

Note: Although this is the preferred option and would be deemed as good practice to upgrade an existing 'gravity fed' circuit to 'fully pumped', if this is impracticable, it can be retained. However, the controls would need to be upgraded to include a cylinder thermostat and zone valve to control the water temperature of the hot water circuit and also provide an interlock with the boiler to prevent burner cycling.

Conversion to another gas

Conversion to another gas, if necessary, should be carried out strictly in accordance with the appliance manufacturer's instructions and the kit of parts supplied by them.

Open-flue – floor standing and wall mounted boilers – 2

Introduction

Modern central heating boiler technology allows increased flexibility in room-sealed appliances. It is always recommended therefore to consider their installation instead of an open-flue type. If there is no outside wall to site a room-sealed terminal, consideration should be given to the installation of a fanned draught room-sealed boiler with a vertical chimney system option.

Before commencing the installation of a gas boiler, a check at the survey stage should be made to ensure that the boiler output is capable of satisfying the heating and/or hot water demands. Where the boiler is to be used on a sealed system, the boiler selected should be specifically designed for this purpose and should incorporate the manufacturer's protection devices for use on sealed systems (see **Part 8 General installation details – Wet central heating – Sealed system**).

Restricted locations

Basements and cellars

A boiler fitted with an automatic means of ignition for use with LPG must not be installed in a room or internal space below ground level, e.g. a basement or cellar. This does not preclude the installation of such boilers into rooms which are basements with respect to one side of the building but open to ground level on the opposite side.

Bath or shower rooms

Open-flue gas boilers must not be installed in a room or internal space containing a bath or shower.

This includes any cupboard/compartment or space (e.g. cubicle), which has an air path or connecting door opening into the bath or shower room.

Only room-sealed appliances are suitable for installation and this location should be considered only if there is no alternative location and provided the manufacturer's installation instructions do not preclude this (see **Part 8 General installation details – Wet central heating – Boiler locations – Rooms containing a bath or shower**).

Note: This requirement applies to new installations. An existing open-flue gas boiler installed before 24th November 1984, in such a location, provided it is safe to use, may be serviced or repaired but should be classed as a Not to Current Standards (NCS) installation in line with the current Gas Industry Unsafe Situations Procedure (see also Essential Gas Safety – Domestic – Parts 8 and 10).

Bedroom/bedsitting rooms

Gas boilers of greater than 14kW heat input (gross) installed in a room used or intended to be used as sleeping accommodation must be room-sealed. This includes the installation of a gas appliance in any cupboard/compartment or space (e.g. cubicle), which has an air path or connecting door opening into the bedroom/bedsitting room.

Gas boilers of 14kW heat input (gross) or less may be room-sealed, or, if open-flued, must incorporate a safety control designed to shut down the appliance before there is a dangerous quantity of products of combustion (POC) in the room concerned. This device should be in the form of an atmosphere sensing device (see **Part 13 Definitions**).

Note: These requirements apply to new installations including used or second-hand gas appliances installed after the 1st of January 1996. Existing appliances in these locations, provided they are safe to use, may be serviced or repaired, but should be classed as a Not to Current Standards (NCS) installation in line with the current Gas Industry Unsafe Situations Procedure (see also Essential Gas Safety – Domestic – Parts 8 and 10).

The use of a fixed Carbon Monoxide detector Kite marked to BS EN 50291 may also be worth considering.

Covered passageways

Open-flued fanned draught flue terminals should not be sited within a covered passageway between properties, e.g. terraced properties. Chimney systems terminated in these positions will produce POC, which could contain carbon monoxide (CO) and could accumulate entering habitable areas above the passageway.

Private garages

The Gas Safety (Installation and Use) Regulations 1984 banned the installation of open-flued appliances in private garages to reduce the risk of explosion/fire from hazardous substances such as petroleum vapour. This ban was relaxed on 31st October 1994. The Building Regulations in Scotland, which also placed certain restrictions on this type of installation, have also been relaxed and there is no longer a requirement for a gas appliance in a garage to be room-sealed.

If installing an open-flued boiler in a private garage the appropriate regulations should be followed. It should be noted in addition, some manufacturers may not allow this type of installation. Where gas operatives encounter an existing open-flued gas boiler installed in a private garage the customer should be advised to check their insurance policy, which may be affected by this type of installation.

Protected shafts/stairway

Protected shafts are stairs or other shafts passing directly from one compartment floor to another and are constructed and enclosed in such a way as to prevent the spread of fire or smoke.

An example of a protected shaft can often be found in flats over two storeys high, with individual accommodation on each floor, where the means of access and exit is via the protected stairway.

No gas appliances are permitted in a protected shaft/stairway.

Installation

Foreword

To avoid repetition, general information will be found in **Part 8 General installation details – Wet central heating,** including details on boiler location, gas supply and ventilation.

General

Open-flued boilers covered by this Part can be floor-standing or wall-mounted and must be connected to the gas supply by a permanently fixed rigid pipe. The final connection to the boiler must incorporate an isolating tap and a means of disconnection to facilitate removal for servicing/maintenance etc.

The boiler must be connected to a permanent chimney system and the chimney designed in accordance with the manufacturer's instructions (see also Essential Gas Safety – Domestic – Part 13 for further guidance).

Air supply

All open-flue gas boilers need air for combustion and to assist the safe operation of the chimney. The ventilation opening should be sized and the chimney tested in accordance with the manufacturer's instructions (see also the current British Standard for ventilation requirements: BS 5440-2 and Essential Gas Safety – Domestic – Part 4 for further guidance).

Chimney (open-flue)

Before commencing the installation of an open-flue central heating boiler to an existing chimney system, the correct operation of the chimney should be verified (see Essential Gas Safety – Domestic – Part 14 for further guidance). Reference should also be made to the manufacturer's installation instructions to establish if the boiler is suitable for the chimney type to which it is being connected.

Room-sealed boilers – 3

Introduction

Before commencing the installation of a gas boiler a check should be made at the survey stage to ensure that the boiler output is capable of satisfying the heating and/or hot water demands.

Where the boiler is to be used on a sealed system, the boiler selected should be specifically designed for this purpose by the manufacturer and should incorporate the manufacturer's protection devices for use on a sealed system (see **Part 8 General installation details – Wet central heating – Sealed system**).

Restricted locations

Basements and cellars

A boiler fitted with an automatic means of ignition for use with LPG must not be installed in a room or internal space below ground level, e.g. a basement or cellar. This does not preclude the installation of such boilers into rooms which are basements with respect to one side of the building but open to ground level on the opposite side.

Covered passageways

Natural draught/fanned draught room-sealed flue terminals should not be sited within a covered passageway between properties, e.g. terraced properties. Chimney systems terminated in these positions may cause the POC to re-enter the air inlet duct, creating poor combustion at the burner. Chimney systems terminated in these positions will produce POC, which could contain carbon monoxide (CO) and could accumulate entering habitable areas above the passageway.

Protected shafts/stairway

Protected shafts are stairs or other shafts passing directly from one compartment floor to another and are constructed and enclosed in such a way as to prevent the spread of fire or smoke.

An example of a protected shaft can often be found in flats over two storeys high, with individual accommodation on each floor, where the means of access and exit is via the protected stairway.

No gas appliances are permitted in a protected shaft/stairway.

Installation

Foreword

To avoid repetition, general information will be found in **Part 8 General installation details – Wet central heating**, including details on boiler location and gas supply.

General

All room-sealed boilers need to be connected to the gas supply by a permanently fixed rigid pipe.

The final connection to the boiler must incorporate an isolating tap and means of disconnection to facilitate removal for servicing/maintenance, etc.

Location

The terminal of a room-sealed or a fanned draught room-sealed boiler should not be located over neighbouring property, where the POC can discharge onto neighbouring property, reference should be made to the manufacturer's instructions for siting the flue terminal (see also Essential Gas Safety – Domestic – Part 13 for further guidance).

Combination boilers – 4

Introduction

Modern central heating boiler technology allows increased flexibility in room-sealed appliances. It is always recommended therefore to consider their installation instead of an open-flue type. If there is no outside wall to site a room-sealed terminal, consideration should be given to the installation of a fanned draught room-sealed boiler with a vertical chimney system option.

Before commencing the installation of a gas boiler, a check at the survey stage should be made to ensure that the boiler output is capable of satisfying the heating and/or hot water demands. Where the boiler is to be used on a sealed system, the boiler selected should be specifically designed for this purpose and should incorporate the manufacturer's protection devices for use on sealed systems (see **Part 8 General installation details – Wet central heating – Sealed system**).

Unlike a 'traditional' central heating boiler, a combination boiler is often produced as a complete package, incorporating all the components required to operate and control a full central heating system as well as the capability to provide instantaneous hot water to a number of draw-off taps.

A point to consider before installation is the availability of a water supply of adequate pressure and flow. Most combination boilers use cold water directly from the mains to supply the hot water taps. The rising water main should also be capable of providing other cold water outlets simultaneously. Failure to take this into account can result in an unsatisfactory performance from the appliance, which requires an adequate water pressure and flow rate to activate various controls. The manufacturer will give details of the minimum pressure required. However, a typical figure is between 1 and 1.35bar.

Note: It is also important to ensure the gas supply is adequate for the purpose (see Installation – General in this Part).

Restricted locations

Basements and cellars

A combination boiler fitted with an automatic means of ignition for use with LPG must not be installed in a room or internal space below ground level, e.g. a basement or cellar. This does not preclude the installation of such boilers into rooms which are basements with respect to one side of the building but open to ground level on the opposite side.

Bath or shower rooms

Open-flue combination boilers must not be installed in a room or internal space containing a bath or shower.

This includes any cupboard/compartment or space (e.g. cubicle), which has an air path or connecting door opening into the bath or shower room.

Only room-sealed appliances are suitable for installation and this location should be considered only if there is no alternative location and providing the manufacturer's installation instructions do not preclude this (see **Part 8 General installation details – Wet central heating – Boiler locations – Rooms containing a bath or shower**).

Note: The above requirement applies to new installations. An existing open-flue gas boiler installed before 24th November 1984, in such a location, provided it is safe to use, may be serviced or repaired but should be classed as a Not to Current Standards (NCS) installation in line with the current Gas Industry Unsafe Situations Procedure (see also Essential Gas Safety – Domestic – Parts 8 and 10).

Bedroom/bedsitting rooms

A boiler of greater than 14kW heat input (gross) installed in a room used or intended to be used as sleeping accommodation, must be room-sealed. This includes the installation of a gas appliance in any cupboard/compartment or space (e.g. cubicle), which has an air path or connecting door opening into the bedroom/bedsitting room.

Boilers of 14kW heat input (gross) or less may be room-sealed, or, if open-flued, must incorporate a safety control designed to shut down the appliance before there is a dangerous quantity of POC in the room concerned. This device should be in the form of an atmosphere sensing device (see **Part 13 Definitions**).

Note: The above requirement applies to new installations including used or second-hand gas appliances installed after 1st January 1996. Existing appliances in these locations, provided they are safe to use, may be serviced or repaired, but should be classed as a Not to Current Standards (NCS) installation in line with the current Gas Industry Unsafe Situations Procedure (see also Essential Gas Safety – Domestic – Parts 8 and 10).

The use of a fixed Carbon Monoxide detector Kite marked to BS EN 50291 may also be worth considering.

Covered passageways

Natural draught/fanned draught room-sealed and open-flued fanned draught terminals should not be sited within a covered passageway between properties e.g. terraced properties. In the case of room-sealed appliances, chimney systems terminated in these positions may cause the POC to re-enter the air inlet duct, creating poor combustion at the burner. Chimneys terminated in these positions will produce POC, which could contain carbon monoxide (CO) and could accumulate entering habitable areas above the passageway.

Private garages

The Gas Safety (Installation and Use) Regulations 1984, banned the installation of open-flued appliances in private garages, to reduce the risk of explosion/fire from hazardous substances such as petroleum vapour. This ban was relaxed on 31st October 1994. The Building Regulations in Scotland, which also placed certain restrictions on this type of installation, have also been relaxed and there is no longer a requirement for a gas appliance in a garage to be room-sealed. If installing an open-flued combination boiler in a private garage, the appropriate regulations should be followed.

It should be noted in addition that some manufacturers may not allow this type of installation.

Where gas operatives encounter an existing open-flued gas boiler installed in a private garage the customer should be advised to check their insurance policy, which may be affected by this type of installation.

Protected shafts/stairway

Protected shafts are stairs or other shafts passing directly from one compartment floor to another and are constructed and enclosed in such a way as to prevent the spread of fire or smoke.

An example of a protected shaft can often be found in flats over two storeys high, with individual accommodation on each floor, where the means of access and exit is via the protected stairway.

No gas appliances are permitted in a protected shaft/stairway.

Installation

Foreword

To avoid repetition, general information will be found in **Part 8 General installation details – Wet central heating**, including details on boiler location, gas supply and ventilation.

General

The installation of a combination boiler whether open-flued or room-sealed, wall mounted or floor standing, should follow the general guidelines for open-flue boilers and room-sealed boilers as outlined in this manual.

Most combination boilers have a high gas input rate (typically 32kW (gross) or greater) in order for them to provide a reasonable water flow rate with a 35°C temperature rise. In order for them to achieve this potential, they should have an adequate gas supply. Most 32kW input (gross) combination boilers however, are fitted with a multifunctional gas control valve ½ inch BSP connections and a ½ inch BSP isolating tap which suggests that 15mm pipework is sufficient to meet this demand.

Whilst 15mm will supply this demand, the length of 15mm pipework is generally limited to within 1m of the boiler. The remaining pipework back to the gas meter may have to be increased to 22mm or in some cases 35mm.

On some installations where the pipe run is longer (15m equivalent length or more) or where the boiler has a higher gas input rating (up to 45kW (gross)), the pipe size may have to be increased to 28mm or 35mm (see Essential Gas Safety – Domestic – Part 5 for further guidance).

It is also important – particularly when running a gas supply to high input gas boilers – where a tube cutter is used to cut the pipe that the pipe ends are suitably de-burred. Removing the burr(s) will reduce restriction and turbulence within the pipe and maintain gas flow.

Failure to provide an adequate gas supply is likely to result in a reduction in performance from the boiler and failure to satisfy user expectations.

All gas boilers must be connected to the gas supply by a permanently fixed rigid pipe. The final connection to the boiler must incorporate an isolating tap and means of disconnection to facilitate removal for servicing/maintenance etc.

It is also important to ensure that if the combination boiler is replacing an existing 'standard design' central heating boiler or water heater, that the existing gas supply is of adequate size to provide for the combination boiler based on the highest gas input rating e.g. the hot water usage. If an existing 'plugged point' in the gas supply is to be utilised, that was designed for another appliance for example a gas cooker, then it is doubtful whether it will satisfy the demands of a combination boiler.

The basic components of a combination boiler are shown in Figure 4.1.

Figure 4.1 Basic components of a combination boiler

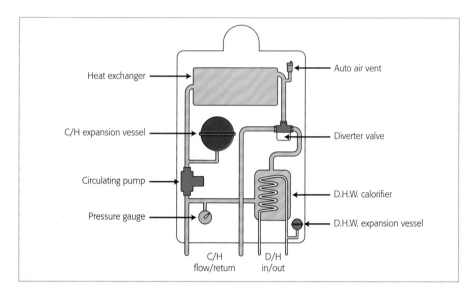

Location

The flue terminal of a natural draught room-sealed or fanned draught room-sealed combination boiler should not be located over neighbouring property, where the POC can discharge onto neighbouring property, reference should be made to the manufacturer's instructions for siting the flue terminal (see also Essential Gas Safety – Domestic – Part 13 for further guidance).

Air supply

All open-flue gas boilers need air for combustion and to assist the safe operation of the chimney. The ventilation opening should be sized and the chimney tested in accordance with the manufacturer's instructions (see also the current British Standard for ventilation requirements: BS 5440-2 and Essential Gas Safety – Domestic – Part 4 for further guidance).

Chimney (open-flue)

Before commencing the installation of an open-flue central heating boiler to an existing chimney system, the correct operation of the chimney should be verified (see Essential Gas Safety – Domestic – Part 14 for further guidance). Reference should also be made to the manufacturer's installation instructions to establish whether the boiler is suitable for the chimney type to which it is being connected.

Sealed system

Because of the increased risk associated with sealed systems as opposed to open systems, extra precautions should be taken to ensure that the installation complies with the requirements of the current Water Supply (Water Fittings) Regulations (see **Part 8 General installation details – Wet central heating – Sealed system**).

Domestic hot water connection

The domestic hot water side of the combination boiler should be connected through the appliance to the cold water main. Where the cold water inlet supply has a non-return valve fitted, e.g. a water meter or stopcock with a loose jumper valve, then the water supply should be fitted with an expansion vessel. The vessel should be fitted between the boiler and valve to accept the expansion of domestic hot water from the boiler. Some boiler manufacturers include this expansion vessel as part of the boiler components. Its size is generally similar to that of a tennis ball (see Figure 4.1).

Water supply areas

Unlike traditional central heating boilers that supply a hot water storage vessel, combination boilers heat the domestic water directly from the cold water main. Consequently, in temporary hard water areas, precautions should be taken to ensure that lime scale build-up does not reduce the efficiency of the domestic hot water calorifier.

To reduce this risk, most combination boilers now incorporate a plate heat exchanger, which, it is claimed, reduces scale build-up. In all cases the boiler manufacturer's installation instructions should be carefully followed.

Note: Water is said to be 'hard' when ordinary soap does not produce an immediate lather. The water contains calcium sulphate and remains permanently hard; the hardness cannot be removed by boiling. 'Temporary hardness' occurs in water that contains calcium bicarbonate, which can be removed by heating the water. This changes the soluble calcium bicarbonate into the insoluble calcium carbonate. As a consequence, the calcium carbonate is deposited in the heat exchanger in the form of 'scale'.

Condensing boilers – 5

Introduction

Before commencing the installation of a condensing gas boiler, a check should be made at the survey stage to ensure that the boiler output is capable of satisfying the heating and/or hot water demands. Where the boiler is to be used on a sealed system, the boiler selected should be specifically designed for this purpose and must incorporate the manufacturer's protection devices for use on sealed systems (see **Part 8 General installation details – Wet central heating – Sealed system**).

Restricted locations

Basements and cellars

A condensing boiler fitted with an automatic means of ignition for use with LPG, must not be installed in a room or internal space below ground level, e.g. a basement or cellar. This does not preclude the installation of such boilers into rooms which are basements with respect to one side of the building, but open to ground level on the opposite side.

Covered passageways

Fanned draught room-sealed flue terminals should not be sited within a covered passageway between properties, e.g. terraced properties. Chimney systems terminated in these positions may cause the POC to re-enter the air inlet duct, creating poor combustion at the burner. Chimney systems terminated in these positions will produce POC, which could contain carbon monoxide (CO) and could accumulate entering habitable areas above the passageway.

Protected shafts/stairway

Protected shafts are stairs or other shafts passing directly from one compartment floor to another and are constructed and enclosed in such a way as to prevent the spread of fire or smoke.

An example of a protected shaft can often be found in flats over two storeys high, with individual accommodation on each floor, where the means of access and exit is via the protected stairway.

No gas appliances are permitted in a protected shaft/stairway.

Installation

Foreword

To avoid repetition, general information will be found in **Part 8 General installation details – Wet central heating**, including details on boiler location and gas supply.

General

The installation of a condensing boiler, whether wall-mounted or floor-standing, should follow the general guidelines for room-sealed boilers as outlined in this part. All gas boilers must be connected to the gas supply by a permanently fixed rigid pipe. The final connection to the boiler must incorporate an isolating tap and means of disconnection to facilitate removal for servicing/maintenance, etc.

Figure 5.1 Condensing boiler

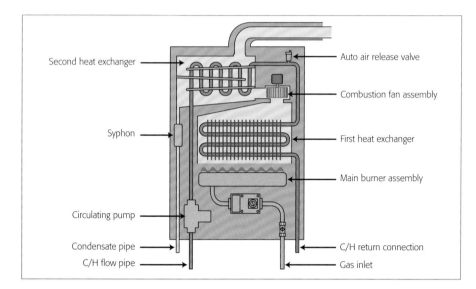

Location

The flue terminal of a room-sealed fanned draught condensing boiler should not be located over a neighbouring property, where the POC can discharge onto neighbouring property, reference should be made to the manufacturer's instructions for siting of the flue terminal (see also Essential Gas Safety – Domestic – Part 13 for further guidance).

System design

In a standard boiler, heat is transferred from the hot POC to the heat exchanger containing the system water. To prevent condensation forming, the boiler heat exchanger is designed so that the POC do not fall below 55°C. This prevents condensation from forming which could cause corrosion and damage the boiler. Also, there would be reduced heat available adversely affecting chimney performance.

The principle difference between a 'standard' boiler and a condensing boiler is that the heat contained in the water vapour of the POC is recovered. A two-phase, single extended surface area heat exchanger or a double pass heat exchanger achieves this. Figure 5.1 shows a typical arrangement.

Figure 5.2 Condensate pipework, terminated externally

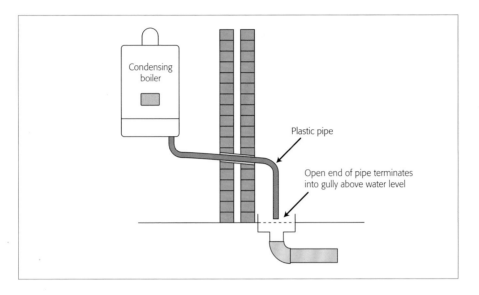

A condensing boiler recovers two types of heat:

1. Sensible heat – this is the heat extracted from the POC as they pass through the first phase or first pass heat exchanger, where the POC temperature is reduced.

2. Latent heat – POC contain water, which, because of the heat of the POC is in the form of a vapour. Heat is recovered from this water vapour by additionally passing the POC through the second part of the heat exchanger.

To take maximum advantage of the increased efficiency, the heating system should be designed to give a flow/return temperature difference of 21°C as opposed to the 11°C for a standard central heating system.

Whilst in the condensing mode, a condensing boiler will produce a significant amount of condensate (a 30kW (gross) boiler in constant operation will produce approximately 4 litres of condensate per hour) which should be removed to a drain or gully.

Where possible, the condensate should discharge into an internal stack pipe; the minimum pipe diameter is 22mm (plastic) and it should be fitted with a trap containing a 75mm condensate seal. It is permissible to discharge via a sink waste through a condensate syphon. In this situation, connection should be made downstream of the sink waste trap.

Where it is not possible to terminate internally, the condensate discharge pipe may be terminated externally (see Figure 5.2). In this case, the condensate pipe may have to be increased in diameter in line with the manufacturer's instructions.

5 – Condensing boilers

Most modern condensing boilers incorporate a syphon trap designed to remove the condensate once it has reached a predetermined level. The condensate should discharge into pipework, which runs internally before passing through the wall. From here the pipework should run to an external drain using the minimum number of joints and bends. This method reduces the risk of the condensate freezing. Earlier boilers without the syphon arrangement allowed a constant trickle of condensate, which was prone to freezing causing the boiler to lock out.

External pipework should be insulated where necessary.

Combined gas fire/back boilers – 6

Introduction

Before commencing the installation of a gas fire/back boiler, a check should be made at the survey stage, to ensure that the boiler output is capable of satisfying the heating and/or hot water demands. Where the boiler is to be used on a sealed system, the boiler selected should be specifically designed for this purpose by the manufacturer and should incorporate the appliance manufacturer's appropriate protection devices for use on sealed systems (see **Part 8 General installation details – Wet central heating – Sealed system**).

Combined gas fire/back boiler installations, are a convenient method of utilising a space to locate a central heating boiler. They are often installed in dwellings that already have an existing builder's opening and brick/masonry chimney. Many houses with this type of installation were built in the latter half of the 19th and earlier part of the 20th century. Consequently, the chimney may be in a poor state of repair and may require additional work prior to installation of the boiler and flexible metallic flue liner. New house designs do however also incorporate this type of installation.

Restricted locations

Basements and cellars

A combined gas fire/back boiler fitted with an automatic means of ignition for use with LPG, must not be installed in a room or internal space below ground level, e.g. a basement or cellar. This does not preclude the installation of such combined appliances into rooms which are basements with respect to one side of the building, but open to ground level on the opposite side.

Bath or shower rooms

An open-flue gas fire/back boiler must not be installed in a room or internal space containing a bath or shower.

Note: The above requirement applies to new installations. An existing open-flue gas fire/back boiler installed before 24th November 1984, in such a location, provided it is safe to use, may be serviced or repaired but should be classed as a Not to Current Standards (NCS) in line with the current Gas Industry Unsafe Situations Procedure (see also Essential Gas Safety – Domestic – Parts 8 and 10).

Bedroom/bedsitting rooms

An open-flue gas fire/back boiler of greater than 14kW heat input (gross) must not be installed in a room used or intended to be used as sleeping accommodation.

An open-flue gas fire/back boiler of 14kW heat input (gross) or less installed in a room used or intended to be used as sleeping accommodation, must incorporate safety controls designed to shut down the appliances before there is a dangerous quantity of POC in the room concerned. These should be in the form of atmosphere sensing devices (see **Part 13 Definitions**).

Note: The above requirement applies to new installations including used or second-hand gas appliances installed after 1st January 1996. Existing appliances in these locations, provided they are safe to use, may be serviced or repaired but should be classed as Not to Current Standards (NCS) in line with the current Gas Industry Unsafe Situations Procedure (see also Essential Gas Safety – Domestic – Parts 8 and 10). The use of a fixed Carbon Monoxide detector Kitemarked to BS EN 50291 may also be worth considering.

Protected shafts/stairway

Protected shafts are stairs or other shafts passing directly from one compartment floor to another and are constructed and enclosed in such a way as to prevent the spread of fire or smoke.

An example of a protected shaft can often be found in flats over two storeys high, with individual accommodation on each floor, where the means of access and exit is via the protected stairway.

No gas appliances are permitted in a protected shaft/stairway.

Approved Document 'J' (ADJ) requirements

Notification of Building Work and Competent Operatives

The Building Regulations Approved Document 'J' (ADJ) that was amended in April 2002, extended the definition of building work requiring notification to Building Control Bodies. An amendment to the regulations called the Building (Amendment) Regulations 2002, defined 'competency' and introduced an exemption from the need to notify.

Building work under ADJ

Open-flue chimneys are defined as 'controlled services' under the Building Regulations. This means that in addition to new chimneys having to meet the requirements of ADJ, if work is to be carried out on existing chimneys then it is important that these also meet the requirements of ADJ. If the work is to involve lining the chimney, either by means of introducing a new or replacement liner, then this is defined as 'building work' under the regulations.

The liner, which may be of rigid, flexible or prefabricated components or may be cast in situ, could alter the flue dimensions and it is, therefore, important that the performance is tested as with a new chimney. In addition if a chimney is to be used for a different type of appliance, an appliance with a different output or is being brought back into use, then it must be tested to ensure it is compliant.

Compliance report

The person carrying out the work is responsible for meeting the requirements of ADJ.

To demonstrate this, when the building work has been completed e.g. installation of a flexible metallic liner or chimney, that person must notify the local authority of the work undertaken.

Government-led changes stipulate that it is now a legal requirement in England and Wales for the relevant Local Authority Building Control to be notified of the installation or exchange of any heat producing appliance (Building Regulations Part J) and associated fittings or services served by the appliance (Building Regulations Part L), within a residential dwelling.

For particular Building Regulations requirements relating to ADJ on the installation of ventilation and chimney systems for gas burning appliances, see also Essential Gas Safety – Domestic – Parts 4 and 13.

Installation

Foreword

To avoid repetition, general information will be found in **Part 8 General installation details – Wet central heating**, including details on boiler location, fireguards, gas supply and ventilation.

General

Gas fire/back boilers are manufactured, tested and approved for installation as a combined unit.

The boiler is not designed for individual installation without the fire, or the fire without the boiler. Generally, radiant convector, radiant convector fuel effect and Inset Live Fuel Effect (ILFE) fire back boiler combinations are available.

An installation 'marriage' using another manufacturer's appliance is not permissible. However, some manufacturers do provide replacement gas fires that can be used to upgrade the fires of their earlier back boiler units. When upgrading such an installation, it is essential that the fire and back boiler are compatible (check with the manufacturer).

Before commencing the installation of a combined gas fire/back boiler see **Part 8 General installation details – Wet central heating – Boiler locations – Builder's opening**. In addition, the correct operation of the open-flue chimney system should be verified (see Essential Gas Safety – Domestic – Part 14 for further guidance).

A chimney serving an open-flue gas fire/back boiler should serve no other appliance and should be routed to ensure full clearance of the POC safely to atmosphere (see Essential Gas Safety – Domestic – Part 14 for further guidance).

Installing a new or replacement fire/back boiler to an existing chimney of proven performance, or to a newly installed chimney system is no guarantee that it will operate correctly i.e. no spillage of POC when tested.

If the gas fire/back boiler is to be installed onto an unlined brick/masonry chimney, the chimney should be lined using a flexible metallic flue liner.

All combined gas fire/back boilers must be connected to the gas supply by a permanently fixed rigid pipe.

The final connection to the boiler must incorporate an isolating tap and means of disconnection to facilitate removal for servicing/maintenance, etc.

Combined gas fire/back boilers are normally installed to an existing brick/masonry chimney and builder's opening. In the absence of an existing opening or chimney, a false chimney breast can be erected to accommodate a flue box enclosure and chimney system (see **Part 8 General installation details – Wet central heating – Flue box/enclosure**). Whichever chimney system is used, the boiler and fire should be installed on a hearth, or be sufficiently high on the wall so as to prevent a fire hazard to carpets, furnishings, etc.

Side wall and shelf protection

The gas fire of the combined unit should be installed so that no part of a combustible wall, when measured laterally from the flame or incandescent radiant source, is less than 500mm, from that radiant source.

The appliance manufacturer's instructions will detail limitations on the height and depth of any shelf above the appliance and detail any protection necessary to prevent the shelf from reaching an excessive temperature.

Air supply

For a combined gas fire/back boiler to clear its POC it is essential that there is adequate ventilation to the room in which it is installed. The ventilation requirements for a fire/back boiler combination should be calculated by adding the maximum heat input ratings of both appliances together in accordance with the manufacturer's instructions (see also the current British Standard for ventilation requirements: BS 5440-2 for further guidance).

Combined gas fire/back circulators – 7

Introduction

Combined gas fire/back circulator installations are a convenient method of utilising a space to locate a domestic hot water circulator. They are often installed in dwellings to replace an existing solid fuel back boiler.

Domestic gas circulators are designed for heating domestic hot water in a hot water storage vessel and as such, are suitable for direct connection to the vessel. Some circulators however, have the capacity not only to heat the domestic hot water, but also a limited number of radiators. These units should be connected using an indirect hot water storage vessel.

Restricted locations

Basements and cellars

A combined gas fire/back circulator fitted with an automatic means of ignition for use with LPG must not be installed in a room or internal space below ground level, e.g. a basement or cellar. This does not preclude the installation of such combined appliances into rooms which are basements with respect to one side of the building but open to ground level on the opposite side.

Bath or shower rooms

An open-flue gas fire/back circulator must not be installed in a room or internal space containing a bath or shower.

Note: This requirement applies to new installations. An existing open-flue gas fire/back circulator installed before 24th November 1984, in such a location, provided they are safe to use, may be serviced or repaired but should be classed as not to current standards (NCS) in line with the current Gas Industry Unsafe Situations Procedure (see also Essential Gas Safety – Domestic – Parts 8 and 10).

Bedroom/bedsitting rooms

An open-flue gas fire/back circulator of greater than 14kW heat input (gross) must not be installed in a room used or intended to be used as sleeping accommodation.

An open-flue gas fire/back circulator of 14kW heat input (gross) or less, installed in a room used or intended to be used as sleeping accommodation, must incorporate safety controls designed to shut down the appliances before there is a dangerous quantity of POC in the room concerned. These should be in the form of atmosphere sensing devices (see **Part 13 Definitions**).

Note: The above requirement applies to new installations including used or second-hand gas appliances installed after 1st January 1996. Existing appliances in these locations, provided they are safe to use, may be serviced or repaired but should be classed as not to current standards (NCS) in line with the current Gas Industry Unsafe Situations Procedure (see also Essential Gas Safety – Domestic – Parts 8 and 10). The use of a fixed Carbon Monoxide detector Kitemarked to BS EN 50291 may also be worth considering.

Protected shafts/stairway

Protected shafts are stairs or other shafts passing directly from one compartment floor to another and are constructed and enclosed in such a way as to prevent the spread of fire or smoke.

An example of a protected shaft can often be found in flats over two storeys high, with individual accommodation on each floor, where the means of access and exit is via the protected stairway.

No gas appliances are permitted in a protected shaft/stairway.

Installation

Foreword

To avoid repetition, general information will be found in **Part 8 General installation details – Wet central heating**, including details on boiler location, gas supply and ventilation.

General

A back circulator is manufactured, tested and approved for installation together with a gas fire as a combined unit. The back circulator is not designed for installation on its own but should always be accompanied by a gas fire approved for such installation by the gas fire/back circulator manufacturer(s).

When upgrading such an installation with a replacement gas fire, it is essential that the fire and back circulator are compatible. This information may only be available from the gas fire/back circulator manufacturer(s).

Before commencing the installation of a combined gas fire/back circulator see **Part 8 General installation details – Wet central heating – Boiler locations – Builder's opening**. The chimney should be designed and tested to ensure correct operation (see Essential Gas Safety – Domestic – Parts 13 and 14 for further guidance).

A chimney serving an open-flue gas fire/back circulator should serve no other appliance and should be routed to ensure full clearance of the POC safely to atmosphere in accordance with the manufacturer's instructions (see also Essential Gas Safety – Domestic – Part 14 for further guidance). Installing a new or replacement fire/back circulator unit to an existing chimney of proven performance, or newly installed chimney system is no guarantee that it will work correctly i.e. no spillage of POC when tested.

All combined gas fire/back circulators must be connected to the gas supply by a permanently fixed rigid pipe. The final connection to the boiler must incorporate an isolating tap and means of disconnection to facilitate removal for servicing/maintenance, etc.

Combined gas fire/back circulators are normally installed to an existing brick/masonry chimney and builder's opening. In the absence of an existing opening or chimney, a false chimney breast can be erected to accommodate a flue box enclosure and chimney system (see **Part 8 General installation details – Wet central heating – Flue box/enclosure**). Whichever chimney system is used, the back circulator and fire should be installed on a hearth or be sufficiently high on the wall to prevent a fire hazard to carpets, furnishings, etc.

Side wall and shelf protection

The gas fire of the combined unit should be installed so that when measured laterally from the flame or incandescent radiant source, no part of a combustible wall is less than 500mm from that radiant source.

The appliance manufacturer's instructions will detail limitations on the height and depth of any shelf above the appliance or any protection necessary to prevent the shelf from reaching an excessive temperature.

Air supply

For a combined gas fire/back circulator to clear its POC it is essential that there is adequate ventilation to the room in which it is installed. The ventilation requirements for a combined gas fire/back circulator combination should be calculated by adding the maximum heat input ratings of both appliances together. Reference should be made to the manufacturer's instructions (see also the current British Standard for ventilation requirements: BS 5440-2 and Essential Gas Safety – Domestic – Part 4).

Unlined brick/masonry chimney

Generally, gas fire/back circulators are designed for fitting to both unlined and lined brick/masonry chimneys. However, there is generally no provision for connecting the back circulator flue outlet directly to any chimney lining. When planning the installation of a liner, reference should be made to **Part 8 General installation details – Wet central heating – Chimney liner – Sealing the annular space between the chimney liner and the brick/masonry chimney** for the method of connection.

Where a gas fire/back circulator is fitted to an unlined chimney, the appliance flue outlet should:

1. Prevent the entry of falling debris into the appliance flue spigot or flue connection piece; and

2. Provide a void of a minimum volume of $12dm^3$ below the lowest point of the appliance flue outlet (see Figure 7.1).

Where a gas fire/back circulator is installed, it should not be necessary to line the chimney provided the flue length does not exceed 10m (external wall) or 12m (internal wall). If, however, a liner is to be installed, it should be installed in accordance with the manufacturer's instructions (see also **Part 8 General installation details – Wet central heating – Brick/masonry chimney liner** for further guidance).

For a gas fire/back circulator connected to an unlined brick/masonry chimney it is not normally necessary to fit a flue terminal in place of, or to, the existing chimney outlet.

Sealing the fireplace opening

The gas fire manufacturer's closure plate must be used when fitting a gas fire to a back circulator. However, it is essential that there is access to the back circulator and the facility to check draught diverter operation. The closure plate may therefore have to be modified and sealed in position in accordance with the gas fire or back circulator manufacturer's instructions. Failure to follow these instructions or to seal the closure plate effectively may lead to spillage of POC from the fire.

The gas fire or back circulator manufacturer will give specific instructions on how to modify the gas fire closure plate and how this should be sealed to the back circulator framework and chimney breast.

Figure 7.1 Typical gas fire/back circulator installation

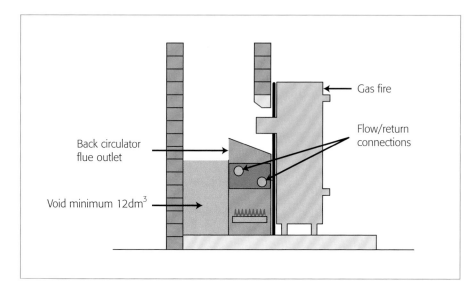

When using a closure plate and an infill panel, if the fireplace opening is too large (see Note). It should be secured and sealed to the fireplace/wall opening or fire surround on all four sides, using an appropriate adhesive tape or other sealing method, e.g. fire cement and screws.

The tape or sealing material should be suitable for the type of surface to which it is to be affixed and needs to be capable of maintaining its seal up to a temperature of 100°C. In this regard it should be noted that proprietary tapes are available which have been developed for this application (i.e. a tape bearing the code PRS 10).

For a successful seal to a tiled fireplace, the surface should be free from dust, polish, grease etc. and if washed, should be dry.

On newly plastered walls or walls with porous surfaces, the plaster or surface should be dry, free of dust, grease, etc. and a sealant applied and dried before any attempt is made to apply sealing tape.

Applying tape to a surface without observing the above rules is almost certain to result in the tape peeling off. This, in turn, will adversely affect flue performance and may cause spillage of POC into the room.

It is also important that the closure plate is not bent or buckled, as this will place undue strain on the seal, which ultimately may cause the seal to fail. Tapes or sealants should have sufficient flexibility to seal along uneven surfaces such as rough stone fireplaces.

When fitting a gas fire/back circulator to a builder's/fireplace opening, combustible material should not be fitted inside this opening.

Figure 7.2 Essential seal when fitting a commercial surround

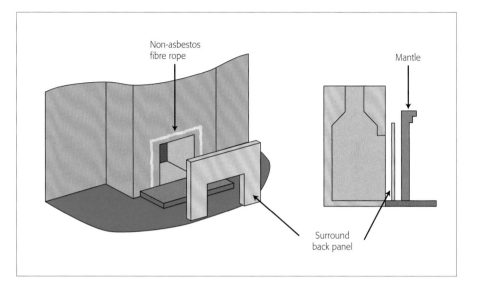

Note: Should the fireplace opening be too large to be closed off with the standard closure plate and back circulator framework, it is acceptable to use an infill panel. It is important that the infill panel is made from fire resisting material having an opening to accommodate the back circulator framework and closure plate. The back circulator framework and closure plate should be secured to the infill panel in such a manner as to facilitate removal of any debris that may fall down the flue.

Warning: The continued safe operation of the combined gas fire/back circulator is dependent on the closure plate and/or infill seal remaining effective until the appliances are next serviced.

Commercially manufactured surrounds

The method of securing the surround to the wall will be found in the manufacturer's installation instructions. However, it is important for the correct operation of the fire/back circulator and the clearance of the POC that there are no gaps between the surround and wall surface, or hearth that will admit air to the builder's opening and chimney (see Figure 7.2).

Where an infill panel is used in conjunction with the surround, it is equally important that this is also sealed to the surround and wall surface to prevent ingress of air to the chimney.

From a gas safety point of view, what should be achieved is an airtight seal which stops ingress of air, adversely affecting chimney performance (see **Sealing the fireplace opening** in this Part).

Equally, the sealing material, as it is within the fireplace opening, should be non-combustible and sufficiently durable to continue to maintain a seal in normal circumstances.

Note: When securing a fire to a commercial surround incorporating a marble or similar infill panel, great care should be exercised to prevent cracking the marble. Bolts, screws and plugs that rely on expansion to secure a grip, should be avoided.

Securing the fire

Although a gas fire is designed to be free-standing when fitted to a back circulator, the fire should be secured to the back circulator framework in accordance with the manufacturer's instructions.

Where it is intended to wall mount the fire, all of the manufacturer's fixing holes should be used.

In all cases especially where dry-lined walls are encountered, it is essential that screws of adequate length and size are used to secure the fire.

Under no circumstances should the fire be 'secured' using proprietary sealing compounds e.g. silicone sealant, unless the manufacturer's instructions state otherwise.

Note: Whatever method is used for securing the fire to the wall, it should be robust enough for the fire to be removed for regular servicing, safety inspection etc.

Gas fire flue spigot restrictor

Traditionally, gas fires are designed as stand alone appliances to be installed using a closure plate to seal off the fire grate opening. With this arrangement the passage of air into the flue will be concentrated on the fire and whatever opening(s) provided by the fire manufacturer in the closure plate. Gas fire manufacturers provide a flue spigot restrictor because they do not know the type of chimney their fire will be installed to or amount of draft that will be created. The flue spigot restrictor is designed to slow down the passage of POC through the fire and thereby improve its overall efficiency.

However, in the case of a fire fitted to a back circulator, provision should be made in the closure plate to allow air for combustion and for the draught diverter operation of the back circulator. The back circulator manufacturer will require a substantial opening under the gas fire – where the closure plate would normally be – for this purpose. As a result, air passing into the chimney is no longer concentrated on passing through the gas fire. Therefore, where a gas fire is fitted as a combined gas fire/back circulator the restrictor should not be fitted to the gas fire spigot unless specified by the appliance manufacturer.

Circulator flow and return circuit

Direct cylinder – Where a back circulator is fitted to a direct hot water storage vessel all domestic hot water installation pipes should be non-ferrous.

A back circulator will often be connected to the existing gravity flow and return pipes and storage vessel connections. However, to improve performance or where a new storage vessel is to be used, the water connections should be fitted as close as practicable to the top of the vessel using a mechanical joint. The return pipe connection should be between 100mm and 200mm from the vessel base.

Any mechanical joints used to connect the flow and return pipes to a direct hot water storage vessel should comply with the requirements of the current Water Supply (Water Fittings) Regulations.

The flow and return pipes from the back circulator to the storage vessel should be at least the same size as the heater connections, normally at least a minimum of 22mm copper pipe.

Horizontal pipe runs should be kept as short as possible, the ratio of horizontal and vertical pipe should not exceed 4 to 1.

Indirect hot water storage vessel – In known temporary hard water areas, back circulators should be connected only to indirect storage vessels, to reduce scale build-up.

General installation details – Wet central heating – 8

8 – General installation details – Wet central heating

General installation details – Wet central heating – 8

8 – General installation details – Wet central heating

Figures

Tables

Introduction

The following offers general guidance notes on the installation of new and replacement central heating boilers and fire/back boiler/circulators, common to most of the appliances covered in this Part.

Boiler locations

Rooms containing a bath or shower

From 24th November 1984, the Gas Safety (Installation and Use) Regulations require that a boiler installed in a room containing a bath or shower must be room-sealed. Prior to this date there were no restrictions and these installations should be classed as Not to Current Standards (NCS) in accordance with the current Gas Industry Unsafe Situations Procedure (see also Essential Gas Safety – Domestic – Parts 8 and 10).

Boilers (room-sealed appliances only) that are installed in locations that contain a bath or shower fall within the scope of BS 7671:2008 (Requirements for Electrical Installations – IEE Wiring Regulations 17th Edition) and Approved Document P (Electrical Safety) of the Building Regulations (England & Wales).

In these two documents a room containing a bath or shower is classified as a special location due to the increased risks associated with these locations. A person in a bathroom or shower is at greater risk of shock due to a lower body resistance, which could be due to the following:

*   lack of clothing, particularly footwear

*   presence of water reducing contact resistance

*   immersion in water, reducing total body resistance

*   ready contact with earthed metal

*   increased contact area

Therefore bathrooms have been defined by a zonal concept to indicate the type of electrical equipment which can be used within a particular zone. The zones are made up of three areas, which are:

*   Zone 0

*   Zone 1

*   Zone 2

Note: Additional information can also be found in section 701 of BS 7671.

The zones are determined taking account of walls, doors, fixed partitions, ceilings and floors where these effectively limit the extent of the zone. This means that a zone does not extend through a door opening (with a door) nor does it pass through a fixed partition. However the zone does extend through an opening and around a fixed partition without a door (see Figure 8.1).

Boilers should only be installed in a bathroom if there is no other practical location.

If there is no alternative to installing the boiler in a room containing a bath or shower and it can only be located in one of the zones identified above, then it needs to be suitably rated for use in that particular zone. Suitably rated equipment, including boilers are classified using an International Protection Code (IP).

Zones 0, 1 and 2 provide a very practical method of specifying requirements for protection against the ingress of water, protection against electric shock, supplementary bonding, etc. in a specific and unambiguous way.

Figure 8.1 Bathroom zones

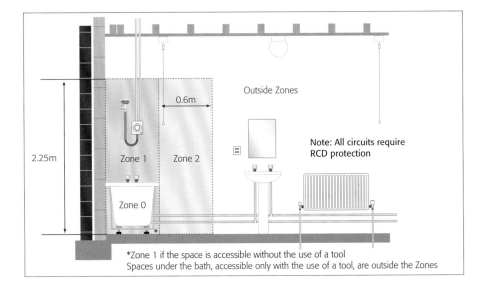

Outside Zones

0.6m

Note: All circuits require
RCD protection

2.25m

Zone 1   Zone 2

Zone 0

*Zone 1 if the space is accessible without the use of a tool
Spaces under the bath, accessible only with the use of a tool, are outside the Zones

Table 8.1 IP Ratings

Digit Value	1st Digit (Solids)	2nd Digit (Liquids)
0	No protection	No protection
1	Protected against objects > 50mm	Protected against dripping water
2	Protected against objects > 12mm	Protected against dripping water when tilted ±15°
3	Protected against objects > 2.5mm	Protected against spraying water
4	Protected against objects > 1.0mm	Protected against splashing water from all directions
5	Dust protected	Protected against water jets
6	Dust tight	Protected against heavy seas
7	Not used	Protected against immersion to > 150mm
8	Not used	Protected against submersion to > 1mm
X	Not solid rated	Not liquid rated

International Protection (IP) Codes

The widely accepted standard IEC 60529 (2001 – 02), which is published by the International Electrotechnical Commission, defines a classification system for the effectiveness of enclosures in preventing the ingress of solids and liquids (see Table 8.1). This system uses two letters – IP (for International Protection) followed by two digits – the first for solids the second for liquids: for example IP 65 implies a dust tight case able to withstand a water jet and is a common level of protection for outdoor equipment.

Zone scenarios

Zone 1

Question – Can a boiler be installed in Zone 1?

Answer – Yes, but the following requirements need to be met:

* the boiler cannot be reasonably located elsewhere

* IPX4 (IPX5 where water jets are likely to be used for cleaning purposes in communal baths or communal showers)

* protected by a 30mA RCD

Question – Can the 230V boiler electrical controls be installed in Zone 1?

Answer – No as the controls will not meet the requirements for use in that zone.

Zone 2

Question – Can a boiler be installed in Zone 2?

Answer – Yes, but the following requirements need to be met:

* the boiler cannot be reasonably located elsewhere

* IPX4 (IPX5 where water jets are likely to be used for cleaning purposes in communal baths or communal showers)

* protected by a 30mA RCD

Question – Can the 230V boiler electrical controls be installed in Zone 2?

Answer – No as the controls will not meet the requirements for use in that zone.

Outside Zones

Question – Can a 13Amp socket outlet be installed in a room containing a bath or shower?

Answer – Yes, as long as it is located 3m from the edge of Zone 1.

Question – Is 30mA RCD Protection required?

Answer – Yes, all circuits within a room containing a bath or shower requires RCD protection.

Question – Do I need to fit an RCD to all circuits on an existing installation wired to a previous edition of the wiring regulations in a room containing a bath or shower?

Answer – No, the work you carryout needs to comply with the current requirements of BS 7671:2008, but you do need to upgrade all of the circuits in that location. Supplementary bonding will be required if there is none present.

Boilers in cupboards within 'Special Locations'

Question – Can a boiler (room-sealed appliance only) with a rating of less than IPX4 be installed in a cupboard at the end of the bath or next to a shower tray?

Answer – Yes, if the boiler cannot be reasonably located elsewhere then this is acceptable as the zones do not extend into an airing cupboard, providing the cupboard has a door. However the boiler and its controls will need to be out of the reach of the person using the bath/shower.

Table 8.2 Requirements for equipment in the Zones

Zone	Minimum degree of protection	Current-using equipment	Switchgear and accessories
0	IPX7	Only 12V AC rms or 30V ripple-free DC SELV, the safety source installed outside the zone.	None allowed[1].
1	IPX4 (IPX5 if water jets)	25V AC rms or 60V ripple-free DC SELV or PELV the safety source installed outside zones 0, 1 or 2. The following fixed permanently connected equipment allowed: whirlpool units, electric showers, shower pumps, ventilation equipment, towel rails, water heating appliances, luminaires.	Only 12V AC and 30V DC SELV switches, the source installed outside zones 0, 1 and 2.
2	IPX4[2] (IPX5 if water jets)	Fixed permanently connected equipment allowed. General rules apply.	Only switches and sockets of SELV circuits allowed, the source being outside zones 0, 1 and 2, and shaver supply units complying with BS EN 61558-2-5 if fixed where direct spray is unlikely.
Out of Zones	No requirement	General rules apply.	Accessories allowed and SELV socket-outlets and shaver supply units to BS EN 61558-2-5 allowed. Socket-outlets allowed 3m horizontally from the boundary of zone 1.

[1] The requirements do not apply to switches and controls which are incorporated in fixed current-using equipment suitable for use in that zone or to insulating pull cords or cord operated switches.
[2] The requirement for IPX4 (or IPX5) does not apply to shaver units complying with BS EN 61558-2-5 installed in zone 2 and located where direct spray from showers is unlikely.

Also the appliance manufacturer will need to be consulted to see if the boiler is suitable for use in a bathroom environment. If the boiler is not out of the reach of the person using the bath/shower then it will need to be treated as if it was in Zone 2.

When installing a boiler in any of the zones, the whole of the boiler must be within the designated zone. If it protrudes into a lower zone the lowest zone criteria must be applied.

Question – Can the controls be located in the cupboard at the end of the bath or next to a shower tray?

Answer – Yes, if the controls cannot be reasonably located elsewhere then this is acceptable, as the zones do not extend into an airing cupboard, providing the cupboard has a door. However the controls will need to be out of the reach of the person using the bath.

Also the control manufacturer will need to be consulted to see if the controls are suitable for use within a bathroom environment. If the controls are not out of the reach of the person using the bath/shower then they will need to be treated as if they were in Zone 2.

Question – Can a boiler with a rating of less than IPX4 be installed in Zone 1 or Zone 2 and be boxed in?

Answer – Additional protection can be fitted to cover the boiler to give an adequate IP rating providing the manufacturer can confirm this is acceptable.

BS 7671:2008 states: that every item of equipment shall be of a design appropriate to the situation in which it is to be used or its mode of installation shall take account of the conditions likely to be encountered, including the test requirements of Part 6.

The boiler will also require 30mA RCD Protection if installed in a room containing a bath or shower.

Other requirements

Supplementary Equipotential Bonding may be required to connect together the terminal of the protective conductor of each circuit supplying Class I* and Class II* equipment in Zones 1 and 2 and extraneous-conductive-parts in these zones including the following:

- metallic pipes supplying services and metallic waste pipes (e.g. water, gas)

- metallic central heating pipes and air conditioning systems

- accessible metallic structural parts of the building; (metallic door architraves, window frames and similar parts are not considered to be extraneous-conductive-parts unless they are connected to metallic structural parts of the building)

- metallic baths and metallic shower basins.

Supplementary bonding can be omitted if all the following conditions are met –

- main bonding is installed to extraneous-conductive-parts

- all circuits in the room containing a bath or shower is RCD protected by a 30mA RCD

The supplementary equipotential bonding where required may be provided in close proximity to the location, for example:

- an airing cupboard in the bathroom

- an airing cupboard in a location immediately adjoining the bathroom

- in the loft space above the bathroom

If it is not apparent where supplementary equipotential bonding is installed (if required), reference should be made to the location on the Electrical Installation Certificate or Minor Electrical Installation Works Certificate. Also the supplementary bonding clamps need to be accessible.

* Class I equipment – Equipment in which protection against electric shock does not rely on basic insulation only, but which includes means for the connection of exposed-conductive-parts to a protective conductor in the fixed wiring of the installation.

* Class II equipment – Equipment in which protection against electric shock does not rely on basic insulation only, but in which additional safety precautions such as supplementary insulation are provided, there being no provision for the connection of exposed metalwork of the equipment to a protective conductor, and no reliance upon precautions to be taken in the fixed wiring of the installation.

Summary

1. 30mA RCD protection is required on all circuits and equipment in a location containing a bath or shower.

2. Supplementary bonding is not required if RCDs are fitted and main bonding is in place.

3. Electrical equipment must be suitable for use in the location.

Builder's opening

A back boiler/circulator installed in a fireplace opening should have sufficient space around it for air to circulate and draught diverter operation. The opening should be large enough to accommodate the appliance and comply with the dimensions specified by the manufacturer.

Where the existing flow and return pipes are sited on the opposite side to the boiler connections, the pipes should not cross the front of the boiler or heat exchanger access opening in such a manner that would impair access for servicing. Where the boiler manufacturer provides a left or right handed boiler, the heat exchanger should be reversed to eliminate this problem.

To assist the correct operation of the fire/back boiler/circulator, the builder's opening or enclosure should have only two openings: an entry through and around the rear of the fire and an exit via the chimney. All other openings, gaps and cracks, particularly, those between any surround and the builder's opening, those which exist in respect of an existing underfloor air supply and those made for the passage of gas, water, flue pipes and electric cables, should be sealed.

The material used for sealing should be fire-resistant or non-combustible if used within the fireplace opening.

Note: Where it is necessary to provide ventilation, the air vent should not be installed directly within the builder's opening or fireplace recess (see Flame reversal in this Part).

Pipework protection

Water and gas pipework installed within the builder's opening should be protected from potential corrosion and damage caused by soot and debris that might fall from the chimney. A suitable method of protection is to wrap the pipe with a suitable tape, e.g. PVC tape.

All gas pipes must be sleeved where they pass through solid walls (see Essential Gas Safety – Domestic – Part 5 for further guidance).

Hearth

Where a hearth is required within the builder's opening for a fire/back boiler/back circulator installation, a constructional hearth should be built:

1. It should be constructed of solid, non-combustible material at least:

   a) 125mm thick or;

   b) 25mm thick and placed on non-combustible supports at least 25mm high.

2. It should be capable of supporting the total weight of the back boiler/back circulator and fire.

3. It should extend not less than 150mm from the back and sides of the boiler/back circulator. If there is a wall within 150mm of the back boiler/back circulator, the hearth should extend to that wall. In all installations the hearth should extend to the front of the back boiler or back circulator.

The gas fire/back boiler/back circulator should be secured to the hearth using the manufacturer's securing method.

A hearth should be provided for the fire unless the fire is to be wall-mounted. Where a hearth is required, it should comply with the following:

1. It should be made from fire-resisting material.

2. It should be a minimum thickness of 12mm.

3. It should extend 300mm forward from the back plane of the gas fire.

4. It should extend at least 150mm beyond each edge of the naked flame or incandescent radiant source.

Where it is intended to wall-mount the fire, any flame or incandescent material should be at least 225mm above the floor. Where the floor is likely to be covered, any flame or incandescent materials should be at least 300mm above the floor in order to make allowances for floor coverings beneath the fire.

Note: In the case of an Inset live fuel effect gas fire/back boiler installation, an upstanding edge of 50mm minimum height along the front and sides of the hearth or the installation of a fender 50mm high or more, would discourage carpets or rugs being placed on top of the hearth.

Brick/masonry chimneys

Most gas fire/back boiler/back circulator installations will be installed utilising the existing builder's opening and brick/masonry chimney, which were designed for solid fuel appliances. Consequently, most chimneys will have a deposit of soot adhering to the inner walls of the chimney throughout its length. Contained within the soot will be particles of sulphur. When water (rain) mixes with sulphur, sulphuric and nitric acids are formed which attack the mortar joints and brickwork of the chimney ultimately causing the chimney stack to lean to one side before eventually falling over.

A contribution to the outlined above problem, is condensation within the chimney. Condensation will form when water-laden air or, POC come into contact with a cold surface.

In the case of a gas appliance, the POC produced by the appliance contain water vapour. Typically a 30kW (gross) boiler operating for 1 hour will produce approximately 4 litres of water in vapour form during this period. A 6kW gas fire combined with a 6kW back circulator will produce just under 1.5 litres in the same time period.

Unless steps are taken to prevent this water vapour from condensing onto the cold chimney, condensation will form (see Essential Gas Safety – Domestic – Part 13 for further guidance).

To help prevent condensation from forming, the POC should be kept warm and insulated from the cold brick/masonry chimney. One way of achieving this is to insert a flexible metallic flue liner into the chimney, which is then connected directly to the back boiler using the boiler manufacturer's approved method. In the case of gas fire/back circulator installations (see **Part 7 Combined gas fire/back circulators – Unlined brick/masonry chimney**).

Where the chimney has been used for a fuel other than gas, the chimney should be thoroughly swept prior to the installation of the flexible metallic flue liner (see **Chimney liner** in this Part).

If a gas fire/back boiler is to be installed into an unlined brick/masonry chimney, the chimney should be lined using a flexible metallic flue liner.

Note: Some chimney stacks are designed to be a feature of the dwelling and as such, their size and shape may be larger than normal (i.e. the chimney top may be in excess of 1000mm x 1000mm serving a single chimney). Should this be the case, the chimney top may take on the dimensions of a flat roof and create wind turbulence around the terminal, interfering with the evacuation of the POC (creating intermittent down draught). If this should happen, it may be necessary to raise the terminal by a minimum of 250mm above the 'flat roof effect' created by the chimney stack.

Compartment installations

A compartment is an enclosure specifically designed or adapted to house a gas appliance (see Figure 8.2).

Open-flued or room-sealed boilers installed in compartments should comply with the following requirements:

1. The compartment should be a fixed rigid structure.

2. Where the appliance manufacturer's installation instructions do not give specific advice, any internal surface of the compartment, which is constructed of combustible material, should be at least 75mm away from any part of the appliance. Alternatively, the surface should be lined with non-combustible material having a fire resistance of not less than 30 minutes. Materials that comply with the relevant part of BS 476 will meet this requirement.

3. The compartment should incorporate air vents for the provision of air for compartment cooling (if applicable) and where necessary, combustion and correct operation of the flue in accordance with the manufacturer's instructions (see also the current British Standard for ventilation requirements: BS 5440-2 and Essential Gas Safety – Domestic – Part 4 for further guidance).

4. If the compartment houses an open-flue boiler, the door or air vents should not communicate with a bath/shower room. However, where the air vents communicate with a bedroom/bedsitting room the installation should be in accordance with the guidelines in **Part 2 Open-flue – floor standing and wall mounted boilers – Restricted locations – Bedroom/bedsitting rooms.**

5. The compartment should permit access for inspection and servicing of the appliance and any ancillary equipment. In order to discourage its use as a storage cupboard, a notice should be fixed in a prominent position to warn against such use. It should be fitted with a door that will permit withdrawal of the appliance and any ancillary equipment.

Figure 8.2 Compartment installation

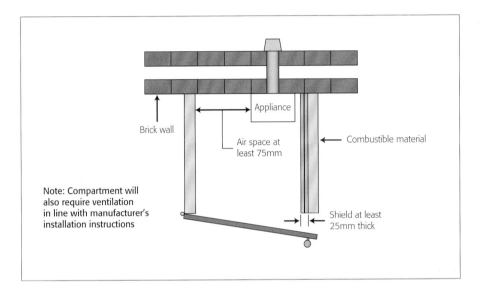

Brick wall

Appliance

Air space at least 75mm

Combustible material

Note: Compartment will also require ventilation in line with manufacturer's installation instructions

Shield at least 25mm thick

Attention: Compartments or cupboards located on an upper floor and containing an open-flued appliance. Care should be taken to ensure that this location does not interfere with the safe operation of any open-flue appliance sited in a downstairs location. Operatives should be aware that under certain adverse weather conditions and where poorly designed chimneys are encountered, open-flues may fail to operate safely and spill POC (see Essential Gas Safety – Domestic – Part 14 for further guidance).

Airing cupboard installations

An airing cupboard is generally sited centrally within a dwelling, often on an upper floor. When it has been necessary to install a central heating boiler in an airing cupboard, the appliance flueing option available was previously limited to the open-flue type.

With advancement in design and technology, this is no longer the case. Modern room-sealed boilers are now available that are fanned draught room-sealed and have a vertical flueing option. Installing this type of boiler and flue option eliminates the historic problem of lint (from the clothes), causing premature blockage of the burner primary airways. This kind of blockage can lead to deteriorating combustion, blockage of the heat exchanger with soot and the inherent risk of fire that has always plagued open-flue boilers in this location, even when the boiler is separated from the airing space.

In addition, siting an open-flue boiler in an upstairs location will require combustion and compartment ventilation. As a result, the dwelling is now flued and ventilated to atmosphere at high level.

In buildings of tight construction, such as timber frame dwellings or where the dwelling has been draught-proofed with double glazing, this arrangement may interfere with the correct operation of the chimney of any open-flue appliance, particularly if it is sited in a downstairs location. The chimney serving the downstairs appliance may be subject to thermal inversion and the appliance subject to spillage of POC into the room (see **Compartment installations** in this Part). Also see Essential Gas Safety – Domestic – Part 14 for further guidance.

Wherever possible, consideration should be given to the installation of room-sealed or fanned draught room-sealed boilers in airing cupboards.

Where a boiler is installed in an airing cupboard, it should comply with the requirements for compartment installations and where combustion air or ventilation is required, this should be installed in accordance with the manufacturer's instructions. See also the current British Standard for ventilation requirements: BS 5440-2 for further guidance. Additionally, the airing space should be separated from the boiler compartment by a non-combustible partition, which should be perforated, by apertures with minor dimensions no greater than 13mm.

Expanded metal or rigid wire mesh are suitable materials for the partition.

Where the boiler is of the open-flued type, the draught diverter and the air vents should be in the boiler compartment. Unless surrounded by an air inlet duct, no chimney should pass through the airing space. An exception can be made if the chimney is protected sufficiently to prevent damage to the airing space contents.

Double-walled flue pipe conforming to BS EN 1856-1 may satisfy the requirements for a 25mm air gap from combustible materials.

Single-walled flue pipe up to 1m from the draught diverter outlet connection should be protected by an air gap of at least 25mm. This air gap may be provided by a non-combustible guard that forms an annular space around the chimney of not less than 25mm.

Expanded metal or rigid wire mesh are both suitable materials for the guard.

External installations

A boiler installed in an external installation should be either:

1. Specifically described in the manufacturer's literature as being suitable for external installation without the need for additional protection; or

2. Installed in an enclosure capable of providing permanent weather protection.

Where an enclosure is required it should comply with the requirements for compartment installations. In addition, the appropriate Building Regulations must also be followed:

1. There should be within the enclosure, an accessible waterproof means of electrical isolation of the boiler installation (see **Electrical connections** in this Part).

2. The enclosure should be fitted with air vents direct to outside air, both at high and low level.

Note: When providing low level ventilation the vent should not be less than 300mm above ground level.

Any permanent openings in the enclosure, including those in the air vents, should have a minor dimension not greater than 16mm in order to prevent the entry of birds or rodents. However, this dimension should not be less than 6mm in order to minimise the risk of blockage.

Where a boiler is located in an exposed position, such as an external location, roof space or unheated garage, etc., consideration should be given to the requirement for frost protection. When a frost thermostat is fitted, it is recommended that it should be adjusted to operate at 4°C.

Roof space installations

Roof spaces incorporating boiler installations should comply with the following requirements:

1. Vertical clearances should be provided so that the static head requirements of open systems are met.

2. Flooring area for normal use and servicing should be provided under and around the boiler (see Note 1).

3. A permanent means of access to the boiler installation should be provided (see Note 2).

4. Fixed lighting for the boiler installation and access should be provided.

5. A guard should be provided to prevent contact between stored articles and the boiler installation.

6. Frost protection should be considered (see **External installations** in this Part).

Note 1: When installing an open-flue gas boiler, any provision required for the protection of the floor or wall on which the boiler is to be mounted will be detailed in the boiler manufacturer's installation instructions. In the absence of instructions, a non-combustible insulating base of at least 12mm thickness should be provided under the boiler if the floor supporting the boiler is of combustible material.

In the case of a floor-standing boiler, care should also be taken to ensure that the floor on which the boiler is to be placed is capable of supporting the weight of the boiler. Also, should the floor be exposed to a prolonged period of wetness, due to a water leak for example, that its strength would not be impaired (e.g. chipboard flooring supporting a boiler under the above circumstances may collapse under the weight of the boiler).

Equally, in the case of a wall-mounted boiler, the wall should be capable of supporting the weight of the boiler and the correct number, size and length of fixing screws or bolts as recommended by the manufacturer should be used.

Note 2: A permanently fixed retractable roof ladder would be considered to satisfy the requirement for a purpose-designed means of access. A safety guard should be provided around the roof access opening.

Where the boiler is open-flued, ventilation should be provided and the boiler flued in accordance with the manufacturer's instructions. See the current British Standard for ventilation requirements: BS 5440-2 also Essential Gas Safety – Domestic – Part 4 for further guidance.

Where an existing brick/masonry chimney is utilised that is not lined, the unused lower portion of the chimney should be sealed from the used portion by means of a plate approximately 250mm below the appliance connection to the chimney. This will provide for a catchment area/void for debris collection. An access panel should also be provided in this area, to enable inspection and clearance of any debris.

The operative must ensure that other chimneys in the same chimney stack are not sealed off.

Note: Any openings into the lower portion of an internal chimney i.e. the sealed-off section should be permanently closed off. For a chimney with at least one external face on the outside wall, the sealed section should be ventilated to the external air at high and low level to prevent damp penetration.

Understairs cupboards

A boiler installed in an understairs cupboard should comply with one of the following:

1. Where the premises in which the cupboard is located is no more than two storeys, the cupboard should comply with the requirements for compartment installations.

2. Where the premises in which the cupboard is located is more than two storeys, all the internal surfaces of the cupboard, including the base, should be non-combustible or alternatively, should be lined with non-combustible material having a fire resistance of not less than 30 minutes. Materials that comply with the relevant parts of BS 476 will meet this requirement. The air vents should be direct to outside air and sized in accordance with the manufacturer's instructions. See also the current British Standard for ventilation requirements: BS 5440-2 for further guidance.

Note: Stairs are very often the only means of escape in the event of a fire, therefore, this location should only be considered when no other practicable position is available.

Clearances around the boiler

When installing the boiler, reference should be made to the manufacturer's instructions for clearances around the boiler. These clearances are to ensure sufficient air circulation for draught diverter operation, fireproofing (where necessary), servicing and maintenance (see **Boiler locations** in this Part).

Note: Some manufacturers recommend clearances in excess of 100mm but claim that the boiler can be serviced with only a 25mm clearance. It is important to note that the additional clearance will be required to facilitate changing major components on the boiler without the necessity of removing the boiler from the wall. The manufacturer's required installation clearances should always be followed.

Commissioning

It is the responsibility of the gas operative to ensure that all work has been carried out in accordance with the relevant Regulations (see **Introduction** at the beginning of this Part) and that the gas appliance and installation operate in a safe and satisfactory manner.

When a gas supply is connected to an appliance there is a requirement in the Gas Safety (Installation and Use) Regulations that the appliance must be commissioned. Unless this work can be completed immediately, the appliance must be disconnected from the gas supply and labelled accordingly.

All gas fittings forming part of the installation must be tested for gas tightness and purged of air (see Essential Gas Safety – Domestic Parts 6 and 15 for further guidance). Additional information on LPG soundness testing will be found in the Gas Installer Manual Series – Domestic – LPG – Including Permanent Dwellings, Leisure accommodation Vehicles, Residential Park Homes and Boats.

The manufacturer's commissioning instructions supplied with the appliance should be followed. The following general procedure may be used for appliances covered in this Part. Additional requirements specific to individual appliances are addressed separately after the general procedure.

General procedure

1. Check that the ventilation requirements are correct and in accordance with the manufacturer's instructions. See also the current British Standard for ventilation requirements: BS 5440-2 for further guidance.

2. Check that the flue termination is correct (see Essential Gas Safety – Domestic – Part 13 for further guidance).

3. Where applicable, carry out a flue flow test (see Essential Gas Safety – Domestic – Part 14 for further guidance).

4. Check electrical connections (see **Electrical connections** in this Part).

5. Test all appliance gas connections with non-corrosive leak detection fluid (LDF).

6. Check for correct operation of all control valves and that the ignition system(s) operate(s) correctly.

7. If necessary, adjust the pilot flame, to envelop the thermocouple tip. Ensure that it maintains the flame supervision device (FSD) correctly.

8. If the pilot light is extinguished, no attempt should be made to re-light it for 3 minutes. Check the 'fail safe' operation of the flame supervision device (FSD) in accordance with the manufacturer's instructions (see Essential Gas Safety – Domestic – Part 12 for further guidance).

9. Check that the operating pressure(s), gas rate(s) or both are in accordance with the appliance data plate. Adjust as necessary (see Essential Gas Safety – Domestic – Part 11 for further guidance).

10. Check that all the burners cross light and the flame picture is satisfactory in terms of stability, structure and colour.

11. Where applicable, carry out a spillage test (see Essential Gas Safety – Domestic – Part 14 for further guidance).

12. Check the boiler thermostat is operating correctly.

13. Flush water system (see **System requirements** in this Part).

14. If it is a sealed system, check that the pressure in the pressure vessel is correct and that the system pressure is adequate (see **System requirements - Sealed system** in this Part).

15. Check the boiler/system bypass valve is correctly adjusted (see **System bypass** in this Part).

16. Balance the system (see **Balancing the system** in this Part).

17. Ensure that any compartment warning labels are correctly fixed (see Essential Gas Safety – Domestic – Part 10 for further guidance).

18. Instruct the user on how to operate the appliance(s) and controls.

19. Leave all instructions with the user.

20. Advise the user that the appliance(s) will require servicing/safety checks at a minimum of 12 monthly intervals or at intervals specified in the manufacturer's instructions.

21. Advise the user of any appliance/installation defects in writing. If necessary, the current Gas Industry Unsafe Situations Procedure should be followed (see also Essential Gas Safety – Domestic – Parts 8 and 10 for further guidance).

Note: A gas appliance in normal use will require servicing and checked for safety at 12 monthly intervals. This period is dependent on the amount of use and the type of room or space it is installed in. It may, therefore, require servicing at intervals less than 12 months.

Combination boilers

For a combination boiler to perform to the manufacturer's specification, it is necessary to check and adjust the domestic hot water flow rate through the appliance. Manufacturer's instructions generally specify a preferred water flow rate in litres per minute raised by °C. It will therefore be necessary to check this performance by using a weir gauge (or suitable measuring jug) and thermometer during the commissioning procedure.

Always use a suitable thermometer, either electronic or mercury glass file type. Place the thermometer in the water flow from a draw-off point and leave until the heater has reached its maximum temperature. Adjust the water flow to the heater as necessary against the manufacturer's specification.

Combined gas fire/back boiler/back circulators

Ensure that the builder's opening has been correctly constructed and sealed in accordance with the manufacturer's instructions (see also **Boiler locations – Builder's opening** in this Part for further guidance).

The fire should be commissioned in accordance with manufacturer's instructions. The general procedure guidelines are as detailed in the Gas Installer Manual Series – Domestic – Gas Fires and Space Heaters).

Condensing boilers

1. Check that the flow/return temperature differential is 21°C.

2. Check that the syphon is clear and unobstructed and that the condensate discharge termination is in accordance with the manufacturer's instructions (see also **Part 5 – Condensing boilers** for further guidance).

System bypass

Some boilers, in particular low water content boilers, incorporate or require a system bypass controlled by a valve. The purpose of the bypass is to prevent water overheating and boiling causing noise (kettling) in the boiler. To avoid kettling, the bypass valve should be adjusted so that the flow of water is always above the minimum required to prevent overheating of the boiler. The bypass is usually a minimum of 15mm size and positioned after the circulating pump and installed/adjusted in accordance with the appliance manufacturer's instructions.

Balancing the system

Due to the inevitable restrictions caused by pipework and fittings, water circulation through a central heating system will try to take the easiest route. Balancing the system is therefore essential to ensure that the distribution of hot water reaches all parts of the system. It is important to achieve a temperature difference of 11°C for normal heating systems and 21°C temperature difference for condensing boiler installations measured across the flow and return connections at the boiler. The temperature difference will also need to be measured across individual radiators, the hot water storage vessel and where fitted the system bypass. The circulating pump speed setting will also affect the balancing process and should be adjusted in accordance with the circulating pump manufacturer's instructions.

Servicing

General procedure
(for all appliances when applicable)

The manufacturer's servicing procedure should always be followed. In the absence of instructions, the following general procedure may be used for appliances covered in this manual. However, where there are additional requirements specific to a particular appliance, these are addressed separately after the general procedure.

Preliminary examination

1. Check with the customer to ascertain any problems with the appliance and/or heating system.

2. Check the location of the appliance is suitable (see **Restricted locations** in the relevant Part of this manual).

3. Check for any damage that exists on the appliance and surroundings and advise the customer where appropriate before starting any work.

4. Check the operation of the appliance controls, including thermostats, ignition systems and flame supervision devices.

5. Check the appliance burner flame picture(s).

6. Where applicable, check that the electrical installation complies with the Requirements for Electrical Installations (IEE Wiring Regulations – BS 7671).

7. Check clearances from combustible materials e.g. compartments etc.

8. Check the gas installation pipework for exposure to corrosion/sleeving and clearances from electrical cables.

Full service

1. Isolate the appliance from the gas and water supplies and where applicable the electricity supply (see **Electrical connections** in this Part).

2. Because of the possibility of stray electrical currents, consideration should be given to attaching a temporary continuity bond to the gas supply and the appliance (see Essential Gas Safety – Domestic – Part 5 for further guidance).

3. Remove the main burner for cleaning and wherever possible, the burner should be dismantled and any internal filter or lint arrester gauze removed. Cleaning should be as follows:

   a) All surface dust should be removed using a paint brush or similar.

   b) Using a combination of brushes, remove dust and lint from within the primary air ports, venturi and burner(s).

   c) Check the burner(s) for cracks and metal fatigue.

   d) Investigate the cause of any faults found in c) above and correct. If the gas fire burner is affected (see **Flame reversal** in this Part).

4. Clean the main burner injector(s).

5. Remove the pilot assembly – clean the burner and injector.

6. Check the pilot supply tube is clean and unobstructed.

7. Reassemble the burner(s) and pilot assembly.

8. Check the condition of ignition leads and alignment of the electrode.

9. Access the heat exchanger and thoroughly clean it using a suitable flue brush or tool (see **Heat exchangers** in this Part).

10. Where applicable, examine and clean (where necessary), any fan associated with the appliance or flue.

11. Refit the burner assemblies and check all seals as necessary.

13. If room-sealed, check that the appliance case seals are in good condition, renewing any sealing material as necessary. Also ensure that the case itself fits securely and that all fixing bolts/screws are located correctly (see also **Reports of fumes from room-sealed appliances** in this Part).

14. Restore the electrical supply.

15. If necessary, adjust the pilot flame, to envelop the thermocouple tip. If the pilot light is extinguished, no attempt should be made to re-light the appliance for at least 3 minutes.

16. Test the flame supervision device (FSD) for correct operation (see Essential Gas Safety – Domestic – Part 12 for further guidance).

17. Re-light and check the appliance gas pressure(s), gas rate(s) or both in accordance with the appliance data plate and adjust as necessary.

18. Check the main burner(s) and pilot for satisfactory flame picture.

19. Check the ventilation requirements are correct and in accordance with manufacturer's instructions. See also the current British Standard for ventilation requirements: BS 5440-2 for further guidance.

20. Where applicable, carry out a flue flow and spillage test and check that the flue termination is correct (see Essential Gas Safety – Domestic – Parts 13 and 14 for further guidance).

21. Where applicable, check that the room-sealed terminal is installed correctly (a terminal guard should be fitted where necessary) and that no undergrowth will interfere with combustion and adversely affect flue performance.

22. Check boiler/system bypass valve is correctly adjusted (see **System bypass** in this Part).

23. If it is a sealed system, check that the pressure in the pressure vessel is correct and that the system pressure is adequate (see **System requirements – Sealed system** in this Part).

24. Advise the user to have the appliance(s) serviced/safety checked at a minimum of 12 monthly intervals, or at intervals specified in the manufacturer's instructions.

25. Advise the user of any appliance/installation defects in writing and where necessary, the current Gas Industry Unsafe Situations Procedure should be followed (see also Essential Gas Safety – Domestic – Parts 8 and 10).

Attention: Whilst there are no specific instructions for servicing a multifunctional gas control valve, gas operatives should check that the control knob is free and easy to operate when depressing the pilot control knob to establish the pilot flame. Where this is not the case the plastic knob should be removed and a small amount of the control manufacturer's lubricating oil should be applied to the spindle. Failure to correct this fault could lead to a serious gas escape on the control.

Where gas appliances are fitted with an atmosphere-sensing device (ASD), these devices should be serviced strictly in accordance with the manufacturer's instructions. They are not 'field adjustable'. This means that if a fault develops on, for example, the thermocouple lead, it may be necessary to replace the entire unit. Some manufacturers recommend replacing the ASD every five years (see Essential Gas Safety – Domestic – Part 12 for further guidance).

Note: Gas boilers connected to a fanned draught chimney system should be checked to ensure that the burner will shut down in the event of failure of the draught (refer to manufacturer's instructions).

Where any room or premises is fitted with a fan (e.g. decorative recirculatory ceiling fan, an extract fan, or a fan incorporated within an appliance for example a tumble dryer), the operation of the fan(s) should not adversely affect the performance of the chimney when the appliance is tested in accordance with the manufacturer's instructions (see Essential Gas Safety – Domestic – Part 14 for further guidance).

Combination boilers

See **Commissioning** in this Part.

Combined gas fire/back boiler/ back circulators

Ensure builder's opening has been correctly constructed and sealed in accordance with the manufacturer's instructions (see also **Boiler locations – Builder's opening** in this Part for further guidance).

Examine the gas fire heat exchanger (BBU/back circulator installation) especially at the rear of the radiants, logs or coals locations for cracks and general metal fatigue (see **Flame reversal** in this Part) (also see **Commissioning** in this Part).

Condensing boilers

See **Commissioning** in this Part.

Heat exchangers

Some boiler heat exchangers have flueways that are both horizontal and vertical whilst others have flueways that are difficult to reach and clean. It is important therefore when servicing such boilers, particularly if the heat exchanger is full of soot, that all flueways are clean. Failure to effectively clean these flueways will restrict or prevent the POC from passing through the heat exchanger, which will almost certainly result in the boiler becoming blocked with soot once again. During this period the user may be in danger from carbon monoxide poisoning, especially from open-flued appliances.

Chimney flue blocks and liners

A chimney flue block system or liner serving a gas appliance may over a period of time become restricted with spiders' webs which may cause spillage of the POC into the room. Where this is suspected it will be necessary to clean the chimney along its entire length.

System bypass

See **Commissioning** in this Part.

Central heating system checks

Where a sealed system appliance is installed, check the water pressure is sufficient and all pressure and temperature safety valves operate correctly and discharge to a safe position.

Maintenance

Where any maintenance work is carried out on a gas appliance e.g. clearing a blocked pilot jet etc. there is a requirement in the Gas Safety (Installation and Use) Regulations that requires an operative to examine:

1. The effectiveness of any flue.

2. The supply of combustion air.

3. Its operating pressure or heat input or, where necessary, both.

4. Its operation so as to ensure its safe functioning.

The operative must forthwith take all reasonable practicable steps to notify any defect to the responsible person and where different, the owner of the premises in which the appliance is situated. If neither is reasonably practicable, in the case of an appliance supplied with LPG, the supplier of the gas to the appliance, or, in any case, the transporter must be notified.

Fault finding

Fault finding should always be carried out in a methodical manner. The operation of appliance, burners, control taps, ignition systems, thermostatic controls and flame supervision devices are covered in detail in the appropriate parts of the Essential Gas Safety – Domestic – Parts 1 – 17. However, the following list helps to apply a methodical approach to fault finding.

General fault finding guide

1. Check with the customer to ascertain what particular problems they have been experiencing with the appliance. This will help to pin point any defects.

2. Check the location and general installation requirements for the appliance are in accordance with the manufacturer's installation instructions.

3. Where possible, always refer to the appliance manufacturer's installation/maintenance instructions as they often contain fault finding information including flow charts to guide the operative to a satisfactory conclusion. They may also contain specific information regarding the testing of and replacement of particular parts.

Tables 8.3 and 8.4, list a number of faults and possible causes relating to central heating systems and appliances.

Corrosion and noise

A common problem of wet central heating systems is noise resulting from trapped air circulating within the system and the subsequent need to vent air from radiators in upper rooms. Research has shown that this 'air' is often actually Hydrogen gas created by a reaction between oxygen in the water and various metals within the system.

A by-product of this corrosion process is the formation of ferrous hydroxide and hydrogen. The ferrous hydroxide is slowly converted to magnetite and more hydrogen.

The magnetite forms a black sludge, which settles in the low points of the system and can block circulating pumps, radiators and pipework.

Air can enter the system from a number of sources but the most common sources are from:

1. Leaking radiator valves and fittings on a negative pressure system.

2. Dissolved oxygen in the water from the feed and expansion cistern on a positive/negative pressure system.

3. Water from the open vent pipe 'pumping over' into the feed and expansion cistern on a positive pressure system creating oxygen rich system water.

4. Water from the open vent pipe 'pumping over' momentarily into the feed and expansion cistern, gradually creating oxygen rich system water.

In the case of 1. – a negative pressure system (caused by the incorrect positioning of the circulating pump). This can cause air entrainment into the system through fittings, which show little signs of water leaks but will allow air to 'leak' back into the system once the circulating pump is 'running' (see Figure 8.3).

Table 8.3 Fault finding chart – Systems

Symptom	Possible cause	Remedy
Pumped Central Heating (C/H) – Gravity Domestic Hot Water (DHW): Upstairs radiators hot.	No anti gravity valve fitted or, existing valve not seating correctly.	Fit new anti gravity valve in C/H flow circuit or maintain existing valve.
Reduced or no circulation of hot water to the hot water storage vessel.	No water in circulating pipework.	Check water level/operation of ball valve in feed and expansion cistern.
	Cold feed blocked between feed and expansion cistern and system pipework. NB. Cistern may appear to be full.	Clear blockage.
	Old cylinder thermostatic temperature control valve on return connection to storage vessel seized in closed position.	Maintain or replace valve.
	Air lock in circulation pipes.	Remove air paying particular attention to long horizontal pipe runs under floors. Circulating pipework should rise continuously from boiler to the vessel.
	Insufficient circulation head. NB. There should be a minimum of 1m between the centre of the boiler casting and the storage vessel coil/calorifier.	Lower boiler or raise storage vessel to obtain minimum circulating head.
Indirect single feed storage vessels: Discoloured domestic hot water.	Storage vessel internal expansion vessel too small to accept – expanded system water (air seal(s) have been lost).	Replace storage vessel with correctly sized internal expansion vessel.
Pumped systems general: Water flowing from warning pipe serving C/H feed and expansion cistern.	Hot water storage vessel (direct type) immersion calorifier leaking, allowing water to flow from the domestic cistern to the C/H feed and expansion cistern via the defective immersion calorifier.	Replace immersion calorifier or exchange direct storage vessel for indirect type and appropriate sized feed and expansion cistern.
	Indirect hot water storage vessel coil/heat exchanger leaking (as above).	Replace storage vessel.
	Water levels too high in C/H feed and expansion cistern allowing hot expanded water to reach overflow outlet once system is heated.	Adjust ball valve to provide correct water level.
	C/H feed and expansion cistern too small to accept volume of expansion water when system is heated.	Exchange feed and expansion cistern for correct size.
System noisy.	'Air' in system.	Implement recommendations as outlined under – **Corrosion and noise** in this Part.
	Trapped air in circulating pump.	Release trapped air from pump (see pump manufacturer's instructions).
	Pump reverberating on wooden floor boarding or plasterboard walls.	Replace pump support brackets with ones containing rubber-insulating bushes.
Replacement pump fails to circulate water.	Air trapped in pump.	Remove air by following manufacturer's commissioning instructions.
No air or water flowing from air release valves, on a system incorporating a close-coupled feed and vent arrangement. NB. Feed and expansion cistern may contain water.	Cold feed blocked at junction with system pipework. Suspect dissolved oxygen-entering system.	Increase cold feed pipe size from CH feed and expansion cistern so that it contains at least 3% of the system water (see **Corrosion and noise** in this Part).

Table 8.3 Fault finding chart – Systems (continued)

Symptom	Possible cause	Remedy
Radiators not very hot.	Boiler thermostat defective.	Replace thermostat.
	Boiler manifold injector tee not fitted (where required) or defective on gravity domestic boiler installations.	Replace or fit new injector tee in accordance with the manufacturer's instructions.
Single pipe systems: Radiator(s) not fully heating up.	Boiler thermostat defective.	Replace thermostat.
	Bore of single pipe circuit too small.	Increase pipe size.
	Single pipe circuit too far from radiator(s).	Relocate single pipe circuit pipework as close as possible to radiator connections.
	Radiator valves closed or partially closed.	Both radiator valves should be fully open.
	Incorrect thermostatic valves used i.e. Two pipe system valves used.	Replace valves with those suitable for a single pipe system. This may involve extending the pipework to a top radiator connection and using inline single pipe thermostatic valves.
	Radiator thermostats shut down after a short period of operation (room still cold). Incorrect valves (see above, also bottom radiator connection used) thermostat sensing head affected by hot air currents from system pipework.	As above.
Two pipe systems: Radiators not fully heating up – downstairs in particular.	System not balanced e.g. too much circulating water delivered to upstairs radiators (15mm or equivalent pipework).	Adjust lock-shield valves on all radiators until there is a temperature differential of 11°C between the flow and return connection to each radiator.
	Unrestricted flow to the domestic hot water circuit.	Adjust lock-shield valve on the domestic hot water circuit to give 11°C differential between flow and return pipes.
	Old inline motorised control valve operational but defective – causing restriction to water flow. **Note: Setting the valve to its manual position and operating the system on the domestic hot water setting of the programmer can often prove this.**	Replace valve with modern type.
Radiator fitted with a TRV does not heat up.	During long periods without use (i.e. warm weather), a TRV operating spindle can seize in the closed position holding the valve against its seating.	Free the operating spindle and maintain the TRV as necessary.
Radiator does not heat up but flow and return pipework hot (twin entry valves).	Radiator valve internal flexible return pipe connection misplaced or missing.	Drain radiator and refit or replace missing pipe.
Radiators hot but with reduced convected heat.	Convection fins blocked with lint.	Clean fins using an appropriate boiler flue brush and vacuum cleaner.
Convector radiators hot but with reduced convected heat.	Convection panel fins blocked with paint and/or lint.	Clean as appropriate.
Skirting radiators hot but with little or no convected heat.	Carpet laid and not secured under radiator blocking off air circulation path.	Cut and secure offending carpet.
	Heat exchanger fins blocked with lint.	Clean fins.

Table 8.3 Fault finding chart – Systems (continued)

Symptom	Possible cause	Remedy
Clicking noise from under floors when system is heating up or cooling down.	Circulating pipework in contact with wooden joists and/or floors.	Insulate offending pipework from woodwork.
Electrical room thermostats slow to respond resulting in variations in room temperatures.	Room thermostat incorrectly wired. NB. Room thermostats fitted with an accelerator/anticipator may require the connection of a neutral wire to operate successfully.	Rewire thermostat in accordance with the manufacturer's instructions. This may involve replacing cables to the thermostat with one containing a suitable neutral cable. Alternatively, exchange thermostat for a modern type utilising a thermistor. This type of thermostat may not require a neutral wire.
	Room thermostat installed in the same room where a radiator is also installed which is controlled by a thermostatic radiator valve (TRV). **NB. Such systems are installed to avoid the continuous running of the circulation pump during programmed heating 'ON' periods. The radiator in the room with the room thermostat should not be fitted with a TRV.**	Remove or immobilise TRV in fully open position.

Table 8.4 Fault finding chart – Boilers

Symptom	Possible cause	Remedy
Boilers general: Pilot light goes out.	Pilot light too small.	Clean and/or adjust pilot flame.
	Defective thermocouple.	Replace.
	Room-sealed flue terminal inlet/outlet blocked or obstructed with undergrowth/spiders webs.	Clear obstruction.
	Room-sealed flue terminal in re-entrant position i.e. POC re-entering appliance air inlet duct.	Remove/re-site cause e.g. drainpipe etc. or re-site boiler and flue terminal (see Essential Gas Safety – Domestic – Part 13).
	System pump fails, causing overheat device to operate, breaking electrical connection to thermocouple.	Replace pump and, where appropriate, reset overheat device.
	Overheat device defective.	Replace overheat device, – on NO account must the device be bridged out.
	Overheat device operates – no system bypass or bypass incorrectly adjusted.	Fit or adjust bypass in accordance with the boiler manufacturer's instructions.
	Boiler internal flue seals defective allowing POC to mix with incoming fresh air (vitiated atmosphere).	Replace defective seals.
	Draught diverter missing on open-flue boiler. **NB. This will result in excessive draught through the boiler.**	Fit manufacturer's draught diverter.

Table 8.4 Fault finding chart – Boilers (continued)

Symptom	Possible cause	Remedy
Boiler fails to ignite.	No electricity.	Investigate cause.
	Boiler thermostat or room thermostat not operating/defective.	Adjust setting or replace as appropriate.
	Boiler fan not operating.	Investigate cause and replace as necessary.
	Multifunctional control valve solenoid not operating.	Investigate cause and replace valve or, where appropriate, solenoid operator.
	Motorised valve not operating to provide electricity supply to boiler.	Investigate cause and replace valve or, where appropriate, the synchronous motor.
	Pilot alight but vapour valve fails to open – pilot too short or valve defective.	Clean pilot injector – replace vapour valve as appropriate.
Combination boilers – basic faults: Boiler fails to ignite.	No electricity.	Programmer/room thermostat in 'OFF' period or fuse blown.
	Inadequate gas pressure or no supply.	Check gas is 'ON' at emergency control valve. Check operating gas pressure at meter and boiler inlet connection (see Essential Gas Safety – Domestic – Part 7 for further guidance).
	Air in gas supply.	Purge gas supply pipework (see Essential Gas Safety – Domestic – Part 15 for further guidance).
	System pressure too low.	Re-pressurise system in accordance with the boiler manufacturer's instructions.
Combination boilers – basic faults: Boiler fails to ignite.	Frequent system pressure loss.	Investigate cause (suspect worn radiator valve glands). Check for correct air or nitrogen pressure in the sealed system expansion vessel.
	Inadequate inlet water pressure.	Investigate cause.
	Appliance water filter blocked.	Clean as necessary.

Figure 8.3 Importance of pump position

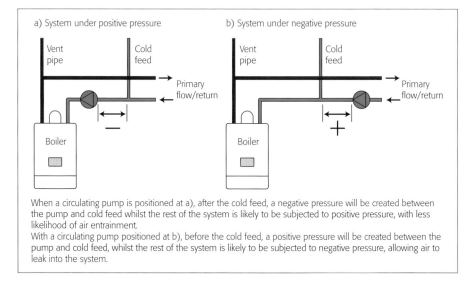

a) System under positive pressure

b) System under negative pressure

When a circulating pump is positioned at a), after the cold feed, a negative pressure will be created between the pump and cold feed whilst the rest of the system is likely to be subjected to positive pressure, with less likelihood of air entrainment.

With a circulating pump positioned at b), before the cold feed, a positive pressure will be created between the pump and cold feed, whilst the rest of the system is likely to be subjected to negative pressure, allowing air to leak into the system.

In the case of 2 – once the system is turned off, water in the feed and expansion cistern – which has absorbed oxygen from the atmosphere – cools down and contracts back into the system and enters the system circulating pipes via the cold feed pipe. If this movement of dissolved oxygen in the water can be contained within the feed and expansion cistern and cold feed pipe it is unlikely to enter the system circulating pipes to cause corrosion. This can be achieved by increasing the cold feed pipe size and/or length so that it contains at least 3% of the system water content, which in the average 3 bedroom semi-detached household, generally means increasing the cold feed pipe size from the 'traditional' minimum 15mm to 22mm diameter.

In the case of 3 – water in the open vent pipe which has been subjected to positive pressure caused by the position of the circulating pump in relation to the open vent and cold feed arrangement, will 'pump over' into the feed and expansion cistern stirring up the sediment and again introducing air into the water. This creates a circuit of its own causing this water to circulate around the system and continually pump over into the feed and expansion cistern. This can generally be overcome by ensuring that the circulating pump is correctly located (see **System requirements** in this Part).

In the case of 4 – water in the open vent pipe, can be subjected to positive pressure (movement). This can happen momentarily when either the circulating pump is turned on or off. The sudden movement of the water causes water to be pushed out of the open vent and into the feed and expansion cistern.

This can generally be overcome by raising the height of the open vent pipe above the feed and expansion cistern to take up the general movement in the water level caused by the operation of the circulating pump, or incorporate a surge arrester in the open vent pipe (see **System requirements** in this Part).

Note: Once the circulating pump is 'running', radiators that are subject to a negative pressure may admit air if the radiator air release valve is opened – to the system as opposed to releasing water.

Figure 8.3, depicts a two-pipe system showing two different circulating pump and cold feed positions.

With the circulating pump positioned, as in Figure 8.3(a), the system will be operating under a positive pressure with less likelihood of air entrainment. However, with a circulating pump positioned as in Figure 8.3(b) before the cold feed connection, with the circulating pump running, this will create a negative pressure and air may be entrained into the system.

Reports of fumes from open-flued appliances

When investigating reports of fumes, or there are signs of spillage from a particular open-flue appliance, but there is no evidence of spillage when the appliance is tested, it may be that under certain conditions (e.g. doors or windows to adjoining rooms open), that the open-flue chimney serving the affected appliance may be subject to thermal inversion (see Essential Gas Safety – Domestic – Part 14 for further guidance).

In such cases, where the dwelling contains other heating appliances e.g. a central heating boiler, gas fire or electric storage heaters etc. and the dwelling is particularly air tight (see below), it may be appropriate when carrying out a spillage test in these situations, that these appliances are operational and the whole house heated.

An open-flued gas appliance installed in an unheated dwelling and relying on adventitious ventilation for correct operation of the flue may, under certain conditions, when tested, pass a spillage test. However, when the same test is applied with the dwelling heated, the appliance under test may be subject to thermal inversion.

This is more problematical with appliances that are installed in buildings that have a greater air tightness. For example:

1. Timber frame buildings or dwellings that have been particularly well draught-proofed, and/or;

2. Where the appliance under test is flued into a chimney on an external wall or has a chimney that is routed externally.

Where an open-flued appliance is affected in this manner, a solution to the problem may be to provide additional ventilation to the room where the appliance is installed (see Essential Gas Safety – Domestic – Part 14 and Using Electronic Combustion Gas Analysers for Investigating Reports of Fumes for further guidance).

Reports of fumes from room-sealed appliances

Natural-draught room-sealed appliances – It is important to ensure that the outer case of a natural-draught room-sealed appliance is fitted correctly. Renew any sealing material as necessary. Ensure that the case itself fits securely and that all fixing bolts/screws are located correctly. Incidents may occur, caused by poorly assembled/maintained room-sealed appliances where POC could escape into the room creating a hazard.

Fanned-flue room-sealed boilers – Instances have occurred where POC have leaked from positive pressure fanned-flue room-sealed, boilers.

Testing appliances with positive pressure cases

There are still a large number of gas appliances in use in customers' homes that utilise positive pressure case technology. Several years ago, the gas industry recognised the dangers that inadequately sealed positive pressure case appliances represent and an agreed procedure was produced to assist gas operatives in recognising the signs and assessing the condition of this type of appliance.

What are 'Positive Pressure Gas Appliances'?

Historically, fanned draught room-sealed boilers were of the positive pressure type. For a positive pressure appliance to operate safely, it is essential to ensure that the combustion chamber casing is firmly secured to the boiler chassis, as the manufacturer intended, with the correct seal in a good condition (see Figure 8.4).

If this is not achieved, there is a real risk that POC may escape into the room in which the appliance is installed and due to the poor combustion that is likely to occur, high levels of carbon monoxide (CO) could be produced creating a dangerous environment. Figure 8.4 shows the differences between positive and negative pressure appliances.

The test procedure

Regulation 26(9) of the Gas Safety (Installation and Use) Regulations (GSIUR) requires an examination of the effectiveness of any flue following work on a gas appliance.

A test method to help ensure that case seals of positive pressure gas appliances comply with the requirements of the GSIUR, has been developed by the Industry and is described below.

Step 1

Before the case is put back on the appliance the following checks should be carried out:

- are any water leaks evident?

- is the backplate or case corroded?

- where corrosion is evident, is it likely to affect the integrity of the case, backplate, or seal?

Note: The extent of the corrosion should be carefully checked with a sharp instrument e.g. a screwdriver. If the instrument does not perforate the corroded area, this should be deemed acceptable, but the gas user should be advised of the problem and potential consequences if a repair is not made.

Figure 8.4 Positive/negative fanned flued room-sealed gas appliances

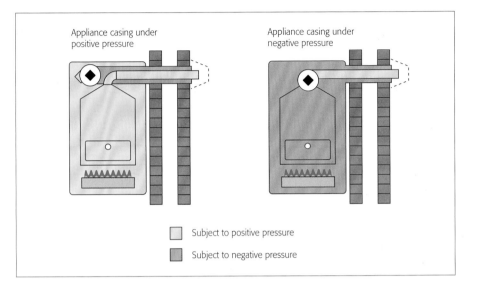

Appliance casing under positive pressure

Appliance casing under negative pressure

☐ Subject to positive pressure

▩ Subject to negative pressure

- are the combustion chamber insulation linings intact?

- is the backplate or the case distorted or damaged? Pay particular attention to the area where the case and seal meet. This may have been caused by explosive ignition of the main burner

- is the case sealing material intact and in good condition? (e.g. pliable, free from discolouration, trapped debris, etc.). Will it continue to form an adequate seal between the case and the backplate?

- is anything trapped or likely to be trapped when the case is put back on (e.g. wires, thermocouple capillaries, tubes, etc.)?

- are other gaskets and seals intact?

- is the pilot inspection glass undamaged?

- are the case fastenings and fixings (including fixing lugs) in good condition? (e.g. screws/nuts stripped)

- are there any signs of discolouration on or around the appliance, which may have been caused by leaks of POC from the appliance?

Rectify any defects identified in Step 1 as necessary and proceed to Step 2.

Note: Where defects are identified they should be classified using the following criteria in accordance with the current Gas Industry Unsafe Situations Procedure.

Where there are inappropriate or missing case fittings or defective seals, which cannot be remedied, but there is no evidence of leakage, the appliance should be classified as At Risk (AR). If there is evidence of actual leakage, then the appliance should be deemed Immediately Dangerous (ID). Where suitable replacement seals are no longer available the appliance should be classed as ID and regarded as obsolete.

Step 2

When the case has been put on the appliance the following checks should be carried out:

- is the case fitted correctly?

- is a 'mark' visible showing that the case had previously been fitted closer to the backplate?

- are all the case screws adequately tightened?

- is a bright area visible on the screw thread of any of the case securing screws, indicating that the screw was previously secured more tightly?

- is anything trapped and showing through the case seal?

Rectify any defects identified in Step 2 as necessary. Proceed to Step 3.

Step 3 – Operate/light the appliance

Ensure that the main burner remains lit (i.e. set the appliance and room thermostats to their highest settings).

Check for possible leakage; initially this can be done by running your hands around the boiler casing and backplate.

Then check for possible leakage etc. as in Step 4 where practicable.

Step 4 – Check for possible leakage of POC from the appliance

Where joints have been disturbed, check with leak detection fluid to confirm that there are no gas escapes.

Check for possible leakage of POC from the appliance using a taper, an ordinary match, or similar (a taper can be used to get into less accessible locations).

Note: Whilst smoke tubes and smoke matches can be used, the results may require further interpretation and these methods are currently being validated.

Light the taper/match and allow the flame to establish. Position the flame very close to the case seal or any possible leakage point (e.g. back panel).

The flame will be blown quite easily by the draught caused by a leak. Move the taper around the entire seal, using fresh tapers as required.

To investigate the seal at the bottom of the case – hold the lit taper between the bottom of the case and the appliance control panel. Does the flame flicker slowly or is it disturbed by leakage flowing from the case? Try the taper in several positions.

Attention: DO NOT confuse natural convection with leakage. DO NOT look for a gas escape with this method.

Rectify any defects as necessary and re-check. If still unsure seek expert advice.

Note: When using this method, be careful not to set fire to surrounding fixtures/furnishings.

Update to the procedure

The Health and Safety Executive (HSE) has advised that a smoke producing device/wand is now available that produces a steady thin stream of smoke which can be used instead of a lighted taper/match and this would be the preferred method to be used.

However, where there is any doubt with regard to the suitability of any smoke producing device/product particularly with reference to COSHH requirements, the original outlined procedure should be followed.

Classifying the installation

British Standard (BS) 5440-1 has been reviewed and the issue of testing positive pressure case seals has been included as an Appendix. There is also some additional text in the form of a 'Commentary on 10.4.2' which states:

"The appliance certification criteria permit a limited amount of case and seal leakage due to manufacturing tolerances. It is therefore likely that some minor leakage might be identified on positive pressure fanned flue boilers, in particular where a thermocouple lead/thermostat capillary or ignition high tension lead etc. passes through a grommet/gasket, or where there is a metal fold/joint that forms a corner on the boiler case itself. In these instances it is necessary to assess whether the leakage is due to normal manufacturing tolerances or to a defect with the grommet/gasket taking into account any previous customer reports of fumes, signs of staining, condition of the grommet/gasket etc., before deciding that the leakage identified is due to normal manufacturing tolerances and whether the appliance is safe to leave in operation.

If there is any concern as to whether the level of leakage is significant and providing the point of leakage is not due to a defect in the main boiler case seal, e.g. around a grommet or gasket, it might be possible to effect a permanent repair by supplementing the original grommet/gasket with high temperature silicone sealant. It is essential that perforations in the case material due to corrosion are not temporarily repaired and any defective main boiler case seals requiring replacement should only be replaced with the manufacturer's supplied or authorised component".

It is essential that in cases where it is determined that any leakage is greater than normal manufacturing tolerances and this can not be rectified at that time, the appliance should be classified as 'Immediately Dangerous' (ID) and made safe in accordance with the current Gas Industry Unsafe Situations Procedure.

Table 8.5 contains a list of room-sealed fan assisted positive pressure gas appliances. This list is not exhaustive, but may be used as guidance to appliances that are believed to operate under positive pressure.

Table 8.5 Room-sealed fan assisted positive pressure gas appliances

Manufacturer and model	Manufacturer and model
Alde International (UK) Ltd Alde 2927 Slimline	**Halstead Heating & Engineering Ltd** Halstead 45F* Halstead 55F* Halstead 65F* Wickes 45F* Wickes 65F* Barlo Balmoral 45F* Barlo Balmoral 55F* Barlo Balmoral 65F*
Brassware Sales Ltd Ferrolli 76 FF* Ferrolli 77 FF*	
Crosslee (JLB) (Pyrocraft) AWB 23. 09 WT Combi	
Crosslee (Trisave Boilers Ltd) Trisave Turbo T45* Trisave Turbo T60* Trisave Turbo 30* Trisave Turbo 22*	**Harvey Habridge Ltd** Impala MK 11 Impala MK 11 Ridgeseal Impala Super 2 (HF) Impala Super 2 (VF)
Glow Worm Ltd Economy 30F* Economy 40F* Economy 50F* Glow Worm Fuelsaver 35F* Glow Worm Fuelsaver 45F* Glow Worm Fuelsaver 55F* Glow Worm Fuelsaver 65F* Glow Worm Fuelsaver 80F* Glow Worm Fuelsaver 100F*	**Potterton Myson Ltd** Myson (Thorn) Olympic 20/35F ‡ Myson (Thorn) Olympic 38/50F ‡ Myson (Thorn) Apollo Fanfare 15/30 Myson (Thorn) Apollo Fanfare 30/50 Supaheat 50/15 with 'A' control Supaheat GC 50/15 Netaheat MK 1 10/16 Netaheat MK 1 16/22 BF Netaheat MK 11 10/16 BF Netaheat MK 11 16/22 BF Netaheat MK 11F 10-16 BF Netaheat MK 11F 16-22 BF Netaheat Electronic 6/10 Netaheat Electronic 10/16 Netaheat Electronic 16/22 Netaheat Electronic 10/16e Netaheat Electronic 16/22e Netaheat Profile 30e Netaheat Profile 40e Netaheat Profile 50e Netaheat Profile 60e Netaheat Profile 80e Netaheat Profile 100e
Glynwed Domestic & Heating Appliances Ltd AGA A50 AGA A50 A AGA A50 NG AGA A50 SS AGA A50 ANG AGA A60 AGA A60 NG AGA A75 NG Hi-light P50 Hi-light P50A SC Hi-light P50S Hi-light P50SS Hi-light P50S/A Hi-light P50S/A GLC Hi-light P50S/A SC Hi-light P50/A Hi-light P70 Hi-light P70S Hi-light P70SS	

Table 8.5 Room-sealed fan assisted positive pressure gas appliances (continued)

Manufacturer and model	Manufacturer and model
Stelrad Group Ltd	**Worcester Bosch**
Ideal Elan 2 40F*	Heatslave 9.24 RSF*
Ideal Elan 2 50F*	Worcester 9.24 Electronic RSF*
Ideal Elan 2 60F*	Worcester 9.24 Electronic RSF 'S'*
Ideal Elan 2 80F*	
Ideal Excel 30F*	
Ideal Excel 40F*	
Ideal Excel 50F*	
Ideal Excel 60F*	
Ideal Sprint 80F*	
Ideal W2000 30F*	
Ideal W2000 40F*	
Ideal W2000 50F*	
Ideal W2000 60F*	

‡ A safety enhancement kit has been designed for these appliances and is available from Potterton Myson Ltd.

* Boilers where spares relevant to case seal problems are still available, based on information provided by manufacturers.

Figure 8.5 Flame reversal (gas fire)

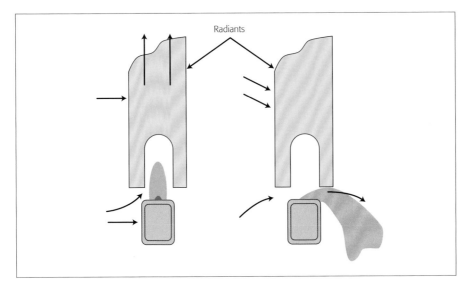

Warning – 'Immediately Dangerous' (ID) installations

It is essential that in ALL cases where spillage is identified, the appliance is made safe. In the case of a new installation when the fault cannot be rectified, it is the responsibility of the gas operative to disconnect and seal the appliance from the gas supply immediately and label the appliance accordingly.

With existing installations, the gas operative should seek permission from the gas user to seal the supply. If permission is refused, the appliance should be turned off and in both instances the current Gas Industry Unsafe Situations Procedure adhered to (see also Essential Gas Safety – Domestic – Parts 8 and 10).

Flame reversal

Flame reversal is a condition where the burner flames are distorted and burn under a gas fire so that they may not be readily seen by the user, (see Figure 8.5). It is often brought to the attention of the gas operative following a complaint of poor radiant effect from the gas fire. The condition may be dangerous and is generally a result of excess air passing into the builder's opening or chimney. This excess air can be as a result of a tall chimney creating too much up draught. More often in the case of a gas fire/back boiler installation, it is the result of an inadequate bottom seal between the flexible metallic flue liner and brick/masonry chimney. Or it is due to other openings within the builder's opening e.g. a ventilation opening, under floor ventilation or pipe ducts, etc.

Another cause may be a fender that is too high or is fitted too close to the gas fire, thereby preventing air from passing under the fire. The condition can be particularly aggravated on windy days.

Note: Due to the method of installation (i.e. a closure plate), a gas fire/back circulator is seldom subject to flame reversal. However, following a complaint of poor radiant effect from the gas fire, the condition should be investigated.

Under normal operating conditions for a gas fire/back boiler, air passes into the builder's opening and chimney under the fire and through the fire heat exchanger and air relief openings on each side of the fire. In abnormal conditions however, (e.g. tall chimney or adverse weather conditions creating an excessive up-draught in the chimney, or other openings within the builder's opening), the excess air will enter the builder's opening from the room by the most direct route, which is generally under the fire and/or downwards through the radiants.

When air passes downwards through the radiants it goes through the gap between the radiant support plate and burner, before finally passing to atmosphere or other rooms. If the gas fire is 'on' at this time, the burner flames will be distorted and will follow the same route as the air, burning under the fire, hence the term, flame reversal.

When investigating a complaint of poor radiant effect from the gas fire and flame reversal is suspected, it is particularly important that the fire front case is in position and completely assembled i.e. boiler control access panel in position where applicable. Failure to place this panel in position will give misleading results (e.g. the excess air will be diverted through the opening and not through the radiants – flame reversal may not occur). Also, wind conditions may not be suitable/appropriate during the visit to create the effect. However, a gas fire subject to flame reversal may bear some visual evidence of the condition.

Below is a list of possible signs of flame reversal:

1. The fire front chrome fender trim may be 'blued' or distorted; or

2. The burner may show signs of distress e.g. it may be discoloured and have surface cracking or severe metal fatigue and corrosion; or

3. The air guide or radiant support plate may be distorted and might show signs similar to 2 above; or

4. The ignition lead may be burnt; or

5. There may be severe distortion and/or splitting of the heat exchanger; or

6. The front bottom outer case may be burnt or distorted.

If instructed to repair the fire, the operative should give the appliance a thorough examination and unless absolutely certain that only superficial damage has occurred, it should be treated as Immediately Dangerous (ID) in accordance with the current Gas Industry Unsafe Situations Procedure (see also Essential Gas Safety – Domestic – Parts 8 and 10). A damaged burner, a misaligned air guide or radiant support plate, or a severely damaged heat exchanger etc. may lead to flame impingement and the production of Carbon Monoxide (CO) which may escape into the room from the damaged appliance.

Wall staining

Discolouration of wall surfaces

Above the fire

All space heaters generate warm air convection currents and transfer heat to any wall surface against which they are placed.

Some modern vinyl wall coverings are affected by heat and are easily discoloured by that heat, which can be confused as staining caused by the spillage of POC into the room.

When investigating such a complaint, the gas operative should be aware of the above possibility but on no account should the report of fumes be dismissed, as a thorough investigation should follow all reports of the possible presence of fumes.

Upper rooms

Some wall staining is also caused by acid attack from within the brick/masonry chimney, caused by water (rain or condensation), mixing with soot to form an acid, which may penetrate the brickwork and appear as a dark brown stain on upper room/bedroom walls spoiling the decor. In this case, a flexible metallic liner installed, will help keep the POC warm and above 'dew point' a point at which condensate forms, thus eliminating the problem.

Odd coloured gas flames

Some gas appliances covered by this part have burner flames that are visible: for example, open-flued boilers and gas fire back boilers/circulators. In the case of gas fires, the burner flames either heat radiants or create realism by passing through a fuel bed simulating solid fuel.

In most cases the burner flames are exposed to the air in the dwelling. This, generally, does not present a problem. However, if a householder suffers with a respiratory condition and uses a Nebulizer to relieve the symptoms, gas operatives should be aware that the gases given off by the respiratory device may affect the flame characteristics and hue. This may, depending upon the concentration of these gases in the room, cause the burner flames to change colour. The colour range may vary from a pale pink to a bright orange.

The flames can also appear to be much larger than normal, as salts in the gases expose the full outer mantle of the flame, which is normally not visible to the naked eye.

The flames will return to their normal characteristic size and colour once the room(s) affected by the gas from the Nebulizer have been purged with fresh air.

Electrical connections

General

All electrical work should comply with the Electricity at Work Regulations.

Also the electrical installation that supplies the gas appliance and its controls should comply with the BS 7671 Requirements for Electrical Installations.

BS 7671 will require electrical certification to be issued to the person ordering the work by the business that carries out the electrical work.

The type of certificate will depend on the amount and type of electrical work undertaken. The two certificates that BS 7671 require to be issued are:

- Electrical Installation Certificate

- Minor Electrical Installation Works Certificate

It is the responsibility of gas operatives to ensure that all electrical work is carried out by a competent person, for example by using an electrician who is a member of a Part P Electrical Competent Persons Scheme.

In the case of a fire/back boiler installation or where installation wiring is routed between the boiler and the outer casing, attention is drawn to the higher ambient temperatures that may exist in the boiler enclosure or casing. Care should be taken to ensure that electrical wiring is not subject to temperatures in excess of that for which it is rated.

Electrical isolation

Electrical isolation should be provided so that all voltage can be effectively 'cut-off' to prevent or remove danger whilst undertaking any work on the appliance. It should also provide an effective, easily operated means of disconnection and be sited to prevent danger.

The electrical supply point should be installed in a readily accessible position, as close as practical, and within easy reach of the appliance (usually 1.5m) and connected in accordance with the manufacturer's installation instructions with regard to, correct method and polarity, fuse rating, earth connection and voltage range.

The method of connection should provide electrical isolation using either:

1. A switched fuse connection unit or;

2. A fused three-pin plug and an unswitched shuttered socket-outlet (except in bathrooms).

Note: In the case of 2, the electrical plug should be removed when servicing the appliance.

Normally the preferred method for isolation will be contained within the manufacturer's installation instructions.

Whichever method of electrical isolation is used it should enable an operative to carry out work on the appliance competently and safely.

In the case of a combined gas fire/back boiler installation where there is an electrical supply to the gas fire, or for a boiler that also requires a permanent 'live' supply, this supply source should be taken from the main supply supplying the boiler/heating system. This will also apply to a boiler that requires a permanent supply for such things as a pump over run.

Important: A separate supply should not be taken from any local electrical circuit.

There should be only one means of electrical isolation controlling the whole boiler installation, failure to ensure this could result in an operative receiving an electrical shock while working on the appliance.

Operative's responsibility

Before commencing work on an appliance or an installation, the gas operative should ensure that it is completely isolated from the electrical supply.

In addition, operatives should ensure that the supply cannot be restored without their knowledge in one of the following ways:

1. Where a switched fused double pole switch is fitted – the fuse carrier should be withdrawn, the fuse removed and a small padlock fitted to the carrier in the open position; or

2. Where a plug and socket outlet is fitted – removal of the plug from the socket and remove the fuse.

Fit a suitable warning notice, this should be attached to the means of isolation stating – 'Danger Do Not Switch On' (Codes: WL28 and/or WL29 - see **Part 14 CORGI Services Limited** Publications).

Note: Further advice on electrical work, is given in the Electricity at Work Regulations as well as BS 7671.

Protective equipotential bonding

The Gas Safety (Installation and Use) Regulations places an obligation on gas operatives who install a section of pipework connecting the primary meter or emergency control valve, whether or not the meter or control are fitted, to inform the responsible person of the possible need for protective equipotential bonding, where such a requirement did not exist before the work was undertaken. They should also explain that such bonding should be carried out by a competent person (see **Electrical connections – General** in this Part). The advice should be in writing and the relevant report form may be used for this purpose (see Essential Gas Safety – Domestic – Part 10 for further guidance).

Although the regulation applies only when new systems are installed and existing ones modified, similar action needs to be taken if a gas operative notices an apparent defect in bonding in other circumstances, e.g. during maintenance checks (this applies to both protective or supplementary equipotential bonding).

In addition to protective equipotential bonding, supplementary bonding of pipework may be necessary in locations of increased risk of electrical shock e.g. bathrooms etc. In such cases, a competent electrical person should be consulted.

The positioning of protective equipotential bonding where fitted to internal and external gas meter installations is shown in Essential Gas Safety – Domestic – Part 5.

Fireguards

Apart from Decorative Fuel Effect (DFE) appliances and some Inset Live Fuel Effect (ILFE) gas fires, most gas fires are fitted with an integral dress guard. The purpose of the guard is to prevent accidental contact between flammable material and the incandescent parts of the appliance. The dress guard may also help to retain artificial logs or coals from tumbling onto the hearth.

Where the gas fire is to be used in the presence of young children, the elderly or infirm it may need to be screened by the addition of a fireguard (CONSUMER PROTECTION – The Heating Appliance (Fireguards) (Safety) Regulations) and preferably attached to the surrounding wall, fireplace surround etc.

Floor and wall protection

When installing an open-flue gas boiler, any provision required for the protection of the floor or wall on which the boiler is to be mounted will be detailed in the boiler manufacturer's installation instructions. In the absence of instructions, a non-combustible insulating base of at least 12mm thickness should be provided under the boiler if the floor supporting the boiler is of combustible material.

In the case of a floor-standing boiler, care should also be taken to ensure that the floor on which the boiler is to be placed is capable of supporting the weight of the boiler. Also, should the floor be exposed to a prolonged period of wetness, due to a water leak for example, that its strength would not be impaired, (e.g. chipboard flooring supporting a boiler under the above circumstances may collapse under the weight of the boiler).

Figure 8.6 Method of installing a combined back boiler/back circulator, in conjunction with a flue box/enclosure and rigid metallic chimney system

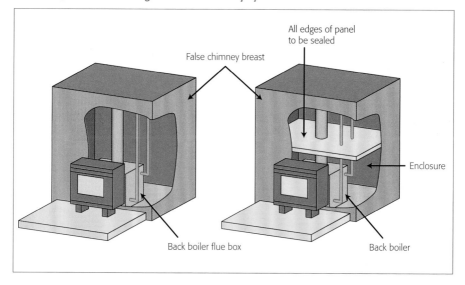

Equally, in the case of a wall-mounted boiler, the wall should be non-combustible or the boiler itself should be suitable for installation to a combustible wall. Also, the wall should be capable of supporting the weight of the boiler and the correct number, size and length of fixing screws or bolts as recommended by the manufacturer should be used.

Note: When installing gas boilers in a timber framed dwelling, there are special requirements for this type of installation (see Gas Installer Manual Series – Domestic – Gas Installations in Timber/Light Steel Frame Buildings).

Chimneys

Flue box/enclosure

In the absence of a suitable existing chimney, a false chimney breast may be erected, or a catchment space adapted to accommodate a suitable flue box or enclosure to which a combined gas fire/back boiler/back circulator can be connected (see Figure 8.6).

Both metallic flue boxes, which comply with BS 715 and propriety flue block concrete enclosures are suitable for use with the back boiler/back circulator. An enclosure that meets the requirements may also be constructed on site using suitable materials. Manufacturer's clearance requirements should always be complied with.

Only rigid metallic chimney systems should be used when connecting to a flue box within a false chimney breast – not a flexible metallic liner. A flexible metallic chimney liner is for use only within a brick/masonry chimney. The chimney should be designed in accordance with the chimney and flue box manufacturer's instructions (see also Essential Gas Safety – Domestic – Part 13 for further guidance).

Unless otherwise specified in the manufacturer's instructions, the fire back boiler/back circulator should be installed to a minimum 125mm diameter flue.

It is important that the flue box and gas fire are stood on a non-combustible base (see **Hearth** in this Part) and installed and secured in accordance with the manufacturer's installation instructions.

All openings including gaps and cracks within the chimney breast should be sealed to prevent the escape of POC to upper rooms e.g. pipe or chimney openings in the ceiling etc.

In the case of a back circulator, the closure plate should be sealed to the front face of the flue box and the fire and back circulator installed in accordance with the manufacturer's instructions (see also the appropriate guidelines of combined gas fires/back circulators in this manual).

Note: Only flue boxes which have been identified as being suitable for use by the back boiler/back circulator manufacturer and/or flue box manufacturer should be used.

Chimney liner

General

The function of the liner is to prevent condensate (water vapour present in the POC which when cooled reverts to a liquid) from cooling and forming on the internal chimney walls. Once formed, the condensate will mix with the existing soot to form an acid. This may penetrate the brickwork and appear as a dark brown stain on upper room/bedroom walls spoiling the decor (see **Wall staining** in this Part). In addition, if the POC are reduced in temperature less heat is available and this could adversely affect flue performance (see Essential Gas Safety – Domestic – Part 14 for further guidance).

Flexible metallic flue liner

When installing a flexible metallic flue liner, it is essential that the liner be installed in one continuous length (no joints are allowed). The liner should be the same diameter as the boiler flue spigot outlet and have a minimum diameter of 125mm where it is serving a gas fire/back boiler/back-circulator. The liner should be connected to the appliance and mechanically held in position (e.g. with a clamp and/or self-tapping screws). It must be sealed to the boiler spigot with fire cement, or by the method approved by the boiler manufacturer.

The method of securing a flexible metallic flue liner in position should be found in the flue liner manufacturer's installation instructions. As a general guide the liner should be secured at the top of the chimney, using the liner manufacturer's flue plate and clamp to support the weight of the liner. The clamp and plate should rest on, and be sealed to, the top of the chimney, leaving sufficient liner to rebuild the flaunching and fitment of an approved terminal.

The flaunching should make a weatherproof joint, leading water away from the liner and terminal. The terminal should always be fitted and provision should be made for adequate space around it to ensure rapid dispersal of the POC.

Note: Due to the age and condition of the chimney (see Chimneys in this Part) the chimney top may have deteriorated to the point where it is difficult to achieve a satisfactory seal at the top of the chimney. In this case, it may be necessary to rebuild the chimney or replace the missing brickwork.

Sealing the annular space between the flexible metallic liner and the brick/masonry chimney

Where the liner enters the builder's opening, the annular space between the liner and chimney should be sealed (see image 'a' in Figure 8.7). This seal is often referred to as a register plate or debris plate. Whilst the plate will certainly 'catch' whatever debris may fall down the chimney, its main function is to prevent any movement of air passing up and around the liner to atmosphere.

In the case of a back boiler, air passing into this annular space should first pass under and through the fire into the builder's opening before passing up the flue to atmosphere. On windy days, this movement of air may be excessive. In this case it will take a direct line generally under the fire and/or down through the gas fire radiants to the builder's opening and flue.

With no seal, or an inadequate seal in place, this movement of air which, apart from cooling the room, may disturb the flames on the gas fire causing flame reversal (see **Flame reversal** in this Part).

In the case of a back circulator unit, these circumstances may not apply because of the closure plate fitted to the front of the builder's opening. However, it will be necessary to effect a seal between the liner and chimney. For a fire/back circulator installation, there is not generally a direct connection between the appliance and the flue opening (see image 'b' in Figure 8.7).

In both cases it is common practice to make the seal using a non-combustible plate suitably secured to the brickwork. Alternatively, if the annular space is not too large, it can be sealed using mineral wool tightly packed into the space. When using this method, the gas operative should ensure that the mineral wool will remain in position for the life of the installation. It is recommended therefore to secure the mineral wool in position using a plate and clamp similar to the one used at the chimney top (see Figure 8.8).

Where the liner connects to the boiler flue spigot, it should be secured and sealed in position in accordance with the manufacturer's instructions. As a general guide, the liner should be secured using self-tapping screws and sealed with fire cement.

A brick/masonry chimney built after 1965 is likely to be constructed with an earthenware liner, in which case there may be no necessity to line the chimney throughout its length. Instead, in the case of a back boiler installation, simply take a short length of liner from the boiler flue spigot and pass it up into the earthenware liner a distance of 150mm (see Figure 8.9).

Figure 8.7 Method of using a flexible metallic liner in a brick/masonry chimney

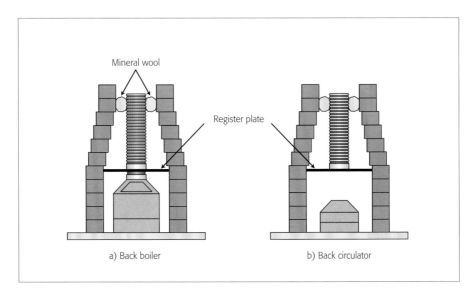

a) Back boiler   b) Back circulator

Figure 8.8 Method of sealing the annular space using mineral wool with plate and clamp

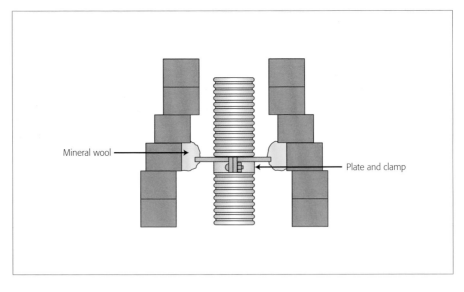

Figure 8.9 Method of securing and sealing a flexible metallic liner to a clay/ceramic liner

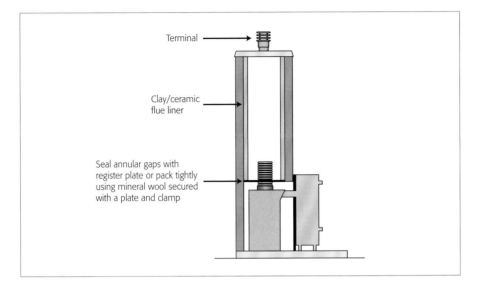

Terminal

Clay/ceramic
flue liner

Seal annular gaps with
register plate or pack tightly
using mineral wool secured
with a plate and clamp

It is important that the gap between the flexible metallic flue liner and salt glazed liner is sealed. This can be achieved by the use of mineral wool tightly packed into the annular space. When using this method the operative should ensure that the mineral wool will remain in position for the life of the installation. It is recommended therefore, to secure the mineral wool in position using a plate and clamp (see Figure 8.8) similar to the one used at the chimney top. A flue terminal should be fitted to the chimney top (see Figure 8.9).

Poured/pumped concrete chimney liners

These are acceptable alternatives to flexible metallic flue liners, but should only be carried out by a competent contractor. Poured/pumped concrete linings should be installed using a method that has been certificated by an accredited test house. Always check to ensure that the lining is mechanically sound before installing any appliance. Brick/masonry chimneys with this type of lining that have been used with another fuel should be swept and carefully examined before use with a gas appliance.

Terminals and noise

The selection of a terminal can have a profound effect on the inhabitants of the room in which the boiler is installed. For example, back boilers are generally installed in a living room with a flexible metallic flue liner connecting the boiler to an approved terminal (generally aluminium). In most cases this combination is satisfactory. However, where a flue terminal is installed in a particularly exposed position, the terminal fins or holes can resonate in the wind, creating noise. This noise is often transmitted via the liner to the living area and in the process, can be amplified. Most users can tolerate the noise as it is often only intermittent. However, where the noise is intolerable it can be reduced and sometimes eliminated by the fitting of a terracotta terminal complying to BS EN 13502. These terminals are also particularly effective at reducing external noise.

Flue testing

On completion of the installation, the appliance must be tested in accordance with the manufacturer's instructions to ensure that POC are not spilling into the room (see also Essential Gas Safety – Domestic – Part 14 for further guidance). Generally however, gas boiler and fire manufacturers have spillage testing instructions specific to a particular model. Where this is the case, this information will be in their installation instructions and may also be found on a data plate attached to the appliance.

Flue testing with decorative re-circulatory ceiling fans present

When carrying out a spillage test on open-flue appliances (particularly in the case of combined gas fire/back boiler/back circulators with an inset live fuel effect gas fire), where there is a decorative re-circulatory ceiling fan fitted in the same room, spillage tests should be carried out with the fan both on and off, at all speeds and where appropriate, in both directions.

Tests have indicated that these fans can disturb air movement in the room to the extent that they can cause spillage of POC to occur where none was present with the fan in the 'off' position.

Natural draught room-sealed boilers

Choosing the terminal position on the outside wall is probably the most critical part of the installation.

For burner flames to burn correctly (complete combustion), POC should readily disperse and pass freely away from the concentric flue terminal (combined air inlet and flue outlet duct) into the atmosphere and not mix with clean fresh air passing through the air inlet duct to the burner.

Little sympathy can be expected, should the gas operative install a boiler to harmonise with kitchen units only for the flue outlet position to be restricted by an adjacent projection outside e.g. buttresses, gate posts, soil pipes, internal or external corners of buildings etc. These are known as 're-entrant' positions i.e. the POC are prevented from being blown away by the wind but re-circulate around the flue terminal and may 're-enter' the appliance via the fresh air inlet duct.

The POC vitiate this fresh air and reduce its oxygen content.

Consequently, this has a profound effect on combustion quality at the burners and is likely (depending on the degree of vitiation) to cause the flames, including the pilot flame, to become ragged and lift off the burner. In the case of the pilot burner, this could eventually lead to cooling of the thermocouple, which in turn could cause the appliance to fail to safety. The condition is particularly aggravated on windy days (see Essential Gas Safety – Domestic – Part 13 for further guidance).

In the examples given, the condition may be regarded as unsafe. If found by a gas operative, the current Gas Industry Unsafe Situations Procedure should be followed (see also Essential Gas Safety – Domestic – Parts 8 and 10).

Conditions similar to those described above will also be experienced if the concentric flue and air inlet duct is cut too short for the wall thickness. In this situation, the air inlet grilles are likely to be obstructed or blocked by cement mortar, which restricts air entrainment and adversely affects the combustion process.

Other 're-entrant' positions that may be encountered are openings into buildings such as doors, windows and ventilators.

Some appliance manufacturers now stipulate particular dimensions where flues should be sited away from openings into buildings and these should always be complied with. In the absence of particular instructions, the operative should seek guidance from the appliance manufacturer.

It is also important that the terminal is positioned so that the POC can safely disperse at all times e.g. when the termination is into a car-port or other similar structure, there should be at least two open, unobstructed sides to that structure. Attention to the material used on the roof and allowance for adequate clearances/protection of the roof should be provided.

Terminals should not be sited into a passageway, pathway or over adjoining property where they can be a nuisance or cause injury (see Essential Gas Safety – Domestic – Part 13 for further guidance).

Some natural draught room-sealed boilers are also suitable for installation onto Se-duct or U-duct chimney systems.

Fanned draught room-sealed boilers

Installation requirements are generally the same as those for natural draught room-sealed boilers, although the siting of a terminal for a fanned draught boiler is not so critical. This is because the fan assists with dispersal of the POC, thereby eliminating most of the problems associated with the siting of natural draught room-sealed terminals.

Whilst the siting requirements are more relaxed, the same precautions as for natural draught room-sealed flue terminations need to be taken, e.g. when the termination is close to openings into buildings or is into a car-port or other similar structure.

Care should also be taken to ensure that the POC and any pluming are not blown onto an adjacent property, causing a nuisance (see Essential Gas Safety – Domestic – Part 13 for further guidance).

Figure 8.10 Vertex flue, a special vertical fanned draught room-sealed flue system

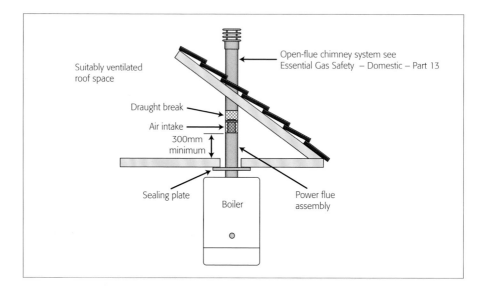

Suitably ventilated roof space

Open-flue chimney system see Essential Gas Safety – Domestic – Part 13

Draught break

Air intake

300mm minimum

Sealing plate

Boiler

Power flue assembly

The boilers are generally designed to incorporate several flueing options with side, rear or vertical flue outlet positions available.

Some fanned draught room-sealed boilers are also suitable for installation onto Se-duct or U-duct chimney systems.

A variation on the vertical flueing option is an arrangement generally referred to as a 'Vertex' flue system, which is available for some types of boilers. With this design, the boiler is generally wall mounted and positioned close to the ceiling adjoining the roof space. A concentric flue arrangement is taken directly from the boiler flue outlet to a position in the roof space, which is defined in the manufacturer's instructions. This position should be at least 300mm above the level of any insulation material in the roof. At this position, a purpose-designed adapter known as a 'draught break' is fitted to the concentric flue system.

From the outlet of the draught break, a conventional secondary chimney system is installed and terminated through the roof in accordance with manufacturer's instructions. The draught break is protected with a guard in the roof area (see Note and Figure 8.10).

Note: This type of flueing arrangement takes its air for combustion from the roof area, which should be ventilated in accordance with the manufacturer's instructions (see Essential Gas Safety – Domestic – Part 4 for further guidance). Where the roof insulation is of a loose fibrous material, care should be taken to ensure that any airborne fibres are not entrained into the appliance through the air inlet duct of the draught break.

Se-duct and U-duct installations

When planning the installation of appliances onto these types of chimney systems, the appliances should be compatible with them and be installed in accordance with the manufacturer's instructions (see also Essential Gas Safety – Domestic – Part 13 for further guidance).

Gas supply

All appliances covered in this part must be connected to the gas supply by a permanently fixed rigid pipe.

When planning the installation of a gas supply for appliances in this part, the installation pipe should be installed in accordance with manufacturer's instructions (see also Essential Gas Safety – Domestic – Part 5 for further guidance).

The final connection to the appliance must incorporate an isolating tap and means of disconnection to facilitate removal for servicing/maintenance, etc.

Where the gas supply is to be taken through a wall it must be sleeved. Where the gas supply is to be buried in the structure or run within the brick/masonry chimney recess, the pipework should be suitably protected from corrosion (for example, coated or wrapped with PVC tape).

System requirements

Open system

A boiler connected to an open system should have a feed and expansion cistern fitted. The cistern should be located at least 1m above the highest point of the circulating system, or at such lesser height as specified in the boiler and circulating pump manufacturer's installation instructions. The cistern should have a capacity of at least 18 litres.

An open vent pipe should be provided from the circulating system to discharge over the feed and expansion cistern above the level of the overflow connection. It should not be less than 22mm diameter, should rise continuously and should be connected in such a position as to prevent discharge of water or ingress of air in all normal conditions of service.

There should not normally be valves or components other than full bore pipe fittings between the boiler and the discharge point of the open vent (see Note).

Note: Except where a boiler manufacturer's installation instructions specifically state otherwise, the open vent and cold feed may be combined. There is no necessity for the system to have a separate open vent, only a cold feed and expansion cistern to accommodate hot, expanded water. When this method is used, the boiler manufacturer's instructions will often stipulate that the combined cold feed and open vent should be not less than 22mm in diameter.

Close-coupled open vent and cold feed arrangement

Appliance manufacturers often specify a close-coupled open vent and cold feed arrangement, where it is not possible to take the cold feed and open vent pipes back to the boiler or where a 'low head' installation is to be installed. Generally, both the open vent and cold feed connections into the system are made into the flow pipe from the boiler. In this arrangement, the circulating pump is also fitted in the flow pipe but after the open vent and cold feed. The general layout for this arrangement is as follows.

The open vent is positioned first in line at a maximum distance away from the boiler, which is defined in the manufacturer's instructions. The cold feed connection is sited downstream of the open vent connection but within 150mm of the open vent. The circulating pump is then sited a short distance downstream of the cold feed connection. With this arrangement, the short distance between the cold feed connection and the inlet of the circulating pump is at a negative pressure, whereas the rest of the system is under a positive pressure.

A distance in excess of 150mm is likely to result in a differential in system pressure between the open vent and cold feed connection. This differential may result in water being discharged from the open vent into the feed and expansion cistern during initial start-up of the circulating pump. Once this occurs water may continue to flow from the open vent due to the syphon effect.

A system affected in this manner is likely to be subject to serious corrosion as a result of system water impregnated with dissolved oxygen continually entering the system.

Note: Care should be taken to ensure that the system control arrangement, does not create a closed off route back to the appliance in the event of a boiler thermostat malfunction. This can be achieved by the inclusion of a system bypass arrangement (see System bypass in this Part).

In some cases, but particularly with low head installations where the ceiling height restricts the height of the open vent pipe, some manufacturers specify a 'surge arrester' in the open vent pipe. This entails the fabrication and installation of a larger diameter section of pipe (greater than 42mm in diameter), which absorbs the movement in the water levels, preventing pumping over (see Figure 8.11 and System requirements in this Part for further guidance). Generally there is no requirement to fit a safety valve to an open system unless the boiler manufacturer specifically asks for one to be fitted.

Air separators

A method of air removal that may be encountered, is the fitting of an 'air separator' in the flow pipe from the boiler. This device provides for a connection onto the open vent and may also include a connection for the cold feed. It is particularly useful during commissioning or any subsequent re-commissioning to quickly remove air from the system water.

The principal behind this device is that any air bubbles held within the heating system water when reaching this device is separated and allowed to vent off through the open vent pipe. Because the volume of the air separator itself is greater than an equal length of flow pipework, turbulence is created causing the water, to momentarily slow down and allow any air in the water to separate and vent off via the open vent (see Figure 8.12).

Figure 8.11 A typical low head installation

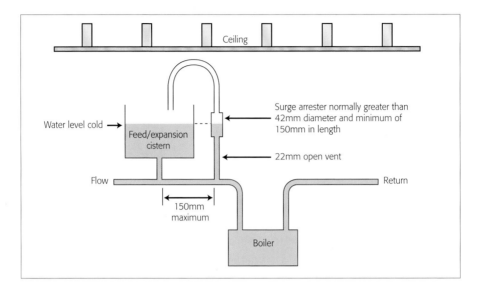

Figure 8.12 A typical water air separator

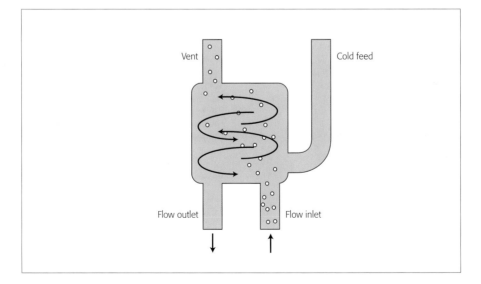

Figure 8.13 Typical sealed system components

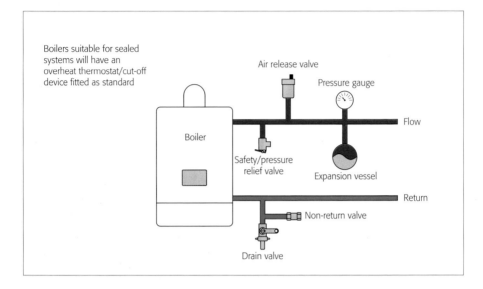

Boilers suitable for sealed systems will have an overheat thermostat/cut-off device fitted as standard

Air release valve

Pressure gauge

Flow

Boiler

Safety/pressure relief valve

Expansion vessel

Return

Non-return valve

Drain valve

Sealed system

Often gas operatives are required to convert an open system into a sealed system. Where this is the case the operative should check the condition of the existing central heating system, (e.g. radiators, valves, etc). These components may be very old and worn and may therefore be prone to leakage and damage when subjected to the higher pressure associated with a sealed system. For example, sealed systems generally operate between 1 and 2 bar as opposed to less than 1 bar pressure in the average two-storey dwelling. Loss of pressure, often resulting in boiler shutdown, can be attributed to leaking radiator valves. Consideration should therefore be given to replacement of these valves during the conversion process.

Some gas boilers can be purchased as a package suitable for installation to a sealed system. They are generally purchased with the appropriate safety devices, components and controls fitted, in which case it is a matter of following the manufacturer's installation instructions and connecting the appropriate pipework to the boiler. However, some manufacturers of 'standard' boilers claim that their boilers are suitable for sealed systems and provide the appropriate overheat device as an optional extra. Figure 8.13 identifies the typical sealed system components. The other components, controls and devices should be purchased separately and fitted to the system.

In all cases in which a boiler is fitted to a sealed system it needs to have the following essential components:

1. An expansion vessel to accept the expanded water.

2. A non-adjustable safety valve (generally pre-set to release at 3 bar pressure).

3. An overheat thermostat acting directly on the gas valve.

4. A pressure gauge with a fill pressure indicator.

5. A filling point with a non-return valve facility.

6. An air release valve.

7. A drain valve.

Where components, 1 and 2 are fitted separately it is important that there are no shut-off valves or restrictions between the expansion vessel and boiler and the safety valve and boiler.

System expansion vessel

The majority of combination boilers installed are fitted to sealed systems. Consequently, there is no expansion cistern to accept the expanded system water once it is heated. In the case of a sealed system, the expansion of water is accommodated by the provision of an expansion vessel, which is generally a component part of the boiler.

Where the expansion vessel is not a component part of the boiler and is located in a position remote from the heating circuit, the connecting pipe between the expansion vessel and the system pipework should have an internal diameter of not less than 13mm.

Its connection with the circuit should be at a point close to the circulating pump inlet in order to maintain positive pressures throughout the system.

The expansion vessel should have a capacity to accept the expansion of the system water when heated from 10°C to 110°C, without raising the pressure in the system to within 0.35bar below the lift pressure of the safety valve.

When designing a sealed heating system or installing a replacement boiler, it is necessary to check that the capacity of the expansion vessel will accept expansion of the system water when heated to 110°C. In the majority of domestic systems the vessel provided by the boiler manufacturer should be adequate. If it is too small, the extra expanding water will be forced out of the safety valve or 'pressure relief valve'. This water will be lost and unless an automatic means has been provided for replenishing this water the cycle will continue until there is insufficient pressure remaining within the system for the boiler to remain operational.

Should this be the case, an additional expansion vessel should be added to the system. Information concerning the calculation of expansion vessel sizes is given in BS 5449.

Filling point

When filling or 'pre-pressurising' a sealed system, the mains water supply may be utilised, providing the connection made complies with the Water Supply (Water Fittings) Regulations. The Regulations require that no supply pipe or secondary circuit should be permanently connected to a closed circuit for filling a heating system, unless it incorporates a back-flow prevention device in accordance with an approved specification.

The previous will normally be satisfied by the use of a temporary connection provided that:

1. The connection is made through a double check valve assembly or some other no less effective device which is permanently connected to that circuit; and

2. The temporary connection is removed after use. Figure 8.14 illustrates a typical method of filling a sealed system.

Overheat thermostat

The overheat device will be a component part of the boiler, or it may be a manufacturer's accessory. The device generally takes the form of a thermocouple interrupter, e.g. a heat sensitive device, fitted to the boiler flow pipe and connected electronically to the thermocouple. When activated, the device breaks the electrical current from the thermocouple to the multifunctional valve, preventing gas passing to the burner.

Safety valve

The safety valve is provided, as a last line of defence to release excess pressure from the system should all other controls fail. Although generally set to release at 3 bar, under fault conditions any release of 'overheated' water from the valve will instantly turn to steam, increasing in volume approximately 1600 times. It is important therefore that a discharge pipe is connected to the valve, terminating in a position where it is clearly visible and where any discharge cannot cause harm to persons or property. For example, where the discharge pipe exits horizontally from the building it is recommended that the discharge point should be faced downwards (see Figure 8.15).

Where the discharge is at low level, the termination point should face downwards (see 'a' in Figure 8.15).

Where the discharge is at high level, if it is impractical to terminate at low level, the termination point should face downwards and back to the wall to prevent scalding water from being ejected causing harm to persons or property (see 'b' in Figure 8.15).

The discharge pipe should be manufactured of a material that will not fail when subjected to high temperatures, e.g. copper pipe.

The discharge pipe should be installed so that there is a continuous fall from the safety valve to the point of termination.

If the safety valve is installed as a separate component, it should be fitted in the flow pipe with no intervening valve or restriction as close as possible to the top of the boiler.

Attention: Any rise in the discharge pipe before termination could trap water which, under winter conditions, could freeze, form an ice plug and render the pipe inoperable.

Pressure gauge with a fill pressure indicator

A pressure gauge with a fill pressure indicator should be fitted permanently to a sealed system. The gauge should be easily seen from the filling point and should preferably be connected at the same point as the expansion vessel.

Existing system

Most central heating boilers are suitable for connection to an existing system. However, to ensure that the new boiler has the best possible start and to reduce potential noise from the boiler, the system should be cleansed using a proprietary central heating system cleanser.

Figure 8.14 Method of filing a sealed system

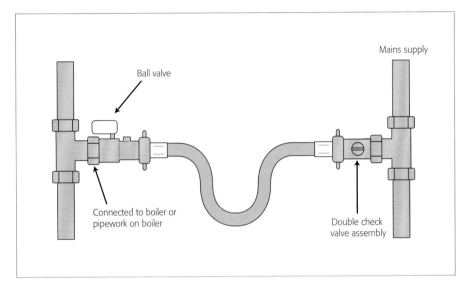

Figure 8.15 Discharge point from a sealed system

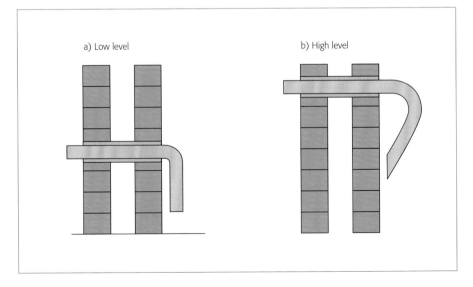

Ventilation

All open-flue gas appliances need air for combustion and to assist the safe operation of the chimney system.

Gas appliances up to 7kW heat input (gross or net) generally do not require ventilation to be provided relying for their correct operation and that of the chimney on adventitious ventilation to the room.

All ventilation requirements for gas appliances should be in accordance with the manufacturer's instructions. See also the current British Standard for ventilation requirements (BS 5440-2) for further guidance.

System water

New system

To ensure a central heating system or back circulator installation has the best possible start and to prolong its operational life, the system should be thoroughly flushed out at least twice with clean water ensuring that all the valves are open – once with cold water and once with hot water. Preferably, the circulating pump should be disconnected and removed from the system for the first flush out.

The flushing process should remove all debris, e.g. steel wool, slivers of copper, flux etc., from within the system.

9 – Warm air heating

Scope

Information contained in this part provides guidance for the installation, service, maintenance and replacement of warm air heating appliances that are 'CE' or British Standard (BS) kite-marked. The information may also be referred to for used or second-hand appliances that do not carry the CE or BS mark but with a data plate bearing information ensuring that the appliance is suitable for the gas type and pressure, i.e. Natural gas at an appliance inlet pressure of 20mbar and Liquefied Petroleum Gas (LPG) Propane and Butane where the supply regulator has been set to provide an operating pressure of 37mbar and 28mbar respectively.

Note: Information in this part should also be read in conjunction with the relevant part of the Gas Installer Manual Series – Essential Gas Safety – Domestic – Parts 1-17.

Introduction

No person shall carry out any work (see **Part 13 Definitions**) in relation to gas appliances and other gas fittings or gas storage vessel covered by this part unless they are competent to do so.

When any work is carried out, gas installing businesses must be registered and their gas operatives must hold a valid certificate of competence for each work activity that they wish to undertake. The certificate must have been issued under the Nationally Accredited Certification Scheme (ACS) for individual gas fitting operatives.

No employer, member of the public or other responsible person should knowingly employ a gas operative who cannot comply with the above requirements.

All appliances must be installed in accordance with the Gas Safety (Installation and Use) Regulations, British Standards, Building Regulations, Regulations for Electrical Installations or those Regulations appropriate to the geographical region in which they are to be installed. Due regard must also be given to the manufacturer's installation instructions.

Information contained in this part has been developed after gathering data and information from various sources, which CORGI Services Limited believes, reflects current custom and practice within the sector.

Background

Similar to wet central heating, warm air heating systems supply heat from a central unit to a number of rooms or spaces. The main difference is that warm air systems use ducts and diffusers and/or registers to distribute the heat rather than pipes and radiators.

Domestic warm air heating systems have been installed for many years, since first being introduced in the mid 1950s. Early heaters had small heat outputs and low fan power. This, combined with the fact that large outlets (registers) had to deliver heat into properties that generally had poor insulation with high heat losses, made them inefficient. They did not provide comfort levels that would be acceptable today. These original heaters employed a belt driven fan, which circulated and distributed warm air through a prefabricated duct system, generally only heating the living room, hall and kitchen areas.

As the warm air heater market expanded, manufacturers designed higher output heaters to be used in conjunction with short, tailor-made ducts, and small side wall registers, all of which improved comfort levels and efficiency.

In 1961 a Government committee produced a report which recommended minimum standards for housing. Heating standards called for temperatures of 18°C in living rooms and 14°C in kitchens and other areas e.g. halls and landings. It was not considered necessary that bedrooms and bathrooms should be heated.

Systems with low side wall registers could be installed cheaply. Many local authorities and private builders fitted them in large quantities. Well over a million systems being installed during the 1960s and 1970s. Other types of warm air heating systems were also designed during this period, such as the 'brick central' or natural convection system (see **Types and application of heaters** in this Part).

Some warm air heaters had water heaters (circulators) integrated into the design to provide domestic hot water. In many dwellings the addition of a separate multi-point water heater was used.

Initially, all warm air heaters were of the open-flue type, but with the introduction and development of high-rise dwellings, room-sealed heaters were designed that operated on 'Se-duct' and 'U-duct' chimney systems. Room-sealed free-standing models were also available (see Essential Gas Safety – Domestic – Part 13 for further guidance).

The modern gas-fired warm air heater has benefited from extensive development, being more compact and fuel efficient than its predecessors. They can provide a number of significant advantages for customers over wet systems, especially in modern highly insulated homes.

1. The freedom to site furniture almost anywhere in a room has a great attraction, especially in smaller homes. Warm air diffusers and registers are much smaller than radiators and can provide an equivalent heat output. Modern fans, which are now directly driven (i.e. they have no fan belt) and sophisticated electronic heating controls deliver the air imperceptibly to maintain a controlled temperature.

2. Fast response to controls, enables rooms to warm up quickly with the heater building up to operating temperature within minutes of being switched on and circulating the warmed air throughout the dwelling (a dwelling that heats up quickly ensures economy and comfort).

3. Warm air systems have the additional advantage of being able to improve the quality of air distributed around the home. Electrostatic air filters can be fitted to the heater to remove pollen and other irritants.

4. In a modern constructed home where draughts are reduced (due to double glazing etc.), warm air provides a clean healthy environment and can introduce fresh air to reduce the possibility of condensation.

5. Some warm air heating systems have a facility to be used in the summer months to provide fresh, filtered air throughout the dwelling. Some models are available with automatic humidity control.

Design of warm air systems

Introduction

The correct design and installation of warm air heating systems is paramount for an efficient and effective heating system and which meets the customers needs.

The following information on the design of warm air heating systems is provided as general guidance only.

General

The necessary information required will include detailed drawings of the building showing the structure, building materials used and their U-values (to calculate heat losses in rooms/spaces). The customer's specification of internal design and desired temperatures (see **Comfort conditions** in this Part) would also be useful.

This information will determine the amount of heat required for each room/space, the duct sizes for the air distribution and return air system and the correct size of the warm air heating appliance. The preparation of a worksheet is helpful to give a logical framework for the calculations.

Note: 10% should be added to the heat loss calculations for each room/space. This margin gives a reserve that allows for different wind conditions and ensures quick response to prolonged periods of cold weather.

Positions of the following should be detailed:

- diffusers/registers
- air distribution/return air duct runs
- return air grilles, return air relief openings
- appliance position
- type and/or route of chimney system
- ventilation grilles

Comfort conditions

The human body is probably at its most comfortable when it is doing the least amount of work. A healthy body should maintain its temperature at a steady 36.9°C.

If the body starts to get cold, the pores close and shivering produces rapid movement in an endeavour to raise the body temperature to normal. On the other hand, when the body becomes too hot, the pores open and sweating occurs. As the moisture evaporates, it takes heat from the body and lowers the temperature.

The body is comfortable when, during any activity, the heat it is producing exactly matches the amount of heat being lost. When the body does not have any work to do its temperature is kept steady.

To give a feeling of freshness there needs to be some air movement in a room. Excessive movement or draughts make us feel cold even when the air temperature is still quite high. In summer, a fan can be used to help us keep cool although it does not actually reduce the air temperature. What it does do is, help to increase the rate at which perspiration is being evaporated. In so doing, it increases the rate at which heat is taken from the body.

Having established the basic requirements for comfort conditions, the next step is to reproduce these conditions in a dwelling. Table 9.1 shows the recommended 'comfortable' temperatures for activities and air changes in a domestic dwelling.

Full central heating should be designed to maintain comfort conditions with an outside temperature of -1°C. However, to reach and maintain the temperatures in Table 9.1 it may be necessary to set the heating controls to their maximum settings in cold conditions.

Table 9.1 Temperature and air changes on which heat loss calculations should be based

Room	Room Temperature °C*	Air Changes per hour‡
Living room	21	1.5
Dining room	21	1.5
Bedsitting room	21	1.5
Bedroom†	18	1
Hall/Landing	18	1.5
Bathroom	22	2
Kitchen	18	2
Toilet	18	2

* These are the temperatures recommended for whole house central heating and for individual rooms with part central heating. Where open-flue appliances are installed the number of air changes should be increased.

‡ Note: Figures in this Table are based on individual rooms that are isolated from each other e.g. with interconnecting doors closed and with the air changes so described. A room that contains a solid fuel chimney and fire grate that is open to the room may be subject to a greater number of air changes – especially if the solid fuel fire or decorative fuel effect gas appliance is alight – in which case it may be difficult to reach the desired temperatures indicated in this Table.

† When bedrooms are used as bedsitting rooms, or for studying purposes, a higher temperature may be required.

Similarly, if a heating system has been turned off overnight or during the day, it is unreasonable to expect that within a short period of turning the heating system on, for the rooms to reach the temperatures shown in Table 9.1, unless an additional heat source is available in the room(s) (e.g. a gas fire).

The fabric of a building or room left unheated will cool. Consequently, it will absorb most of the heat once the heating system is turned on (which may take several hours) and before heat is available to raise air temperature.

A correctly designed warm air heating system is dependent on two major factors – air temperature and air movement. Accurate sized ducts and warm air outlet registers/diffusers should achieve the correct air temperature. Correct air movement is achieved by air velocity through the outlets and the return air ducts/grilles being sized and adjusted to give the required air change in the rooms/spaces.

Figure 9.1 Open-flue and room-sealed flue connections

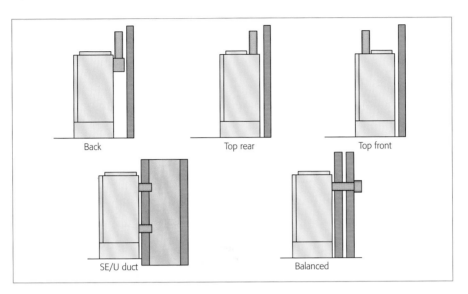

Back   Top rear   Top front

SE/U duct   Balanced

Types and application of heaters

For effective operation, warm air heating systems depend on the continuous circulation of air, which is heated and distributed to one or more rooms, or internal spaces, simultaneously.

Warm air heating appliances fall into two categories, fan assisted and natural convection. Either of these may be combined with a water heating appliance (usually a circulator), to supply domestic hot water. It is important when considering an installation that the type of appliance selected suits the type and size of dwelling.

Further guidance on water heaters can be found in the Gas Installer Manual Series – Domestic – Water Heaters.

Fan assisted model

Warm air is fan assisted through a network of ducts. Displaced air is returned to the heater by means of a series of return air grilles/air relief openings connected by a return air duct to the warm air heater.

The warm air heater should preferably be sited centrally in the dwelling to keep duct lengths, including the return air duct, to a minimum. Some models are room-sealed, but the majority of installations will be open-flue (due to the fact that they need to be centrally located). Heaters are designed with open-flue connections that are located at the back, top rear or top front (see Figure 9.1). They are most frequently fitted in cupboards or compartments, some models utilise any convenient narrow space (slot-fix), or may be free-standing.

Figure 9.2 Basic types of fan-assisted warm air heaters

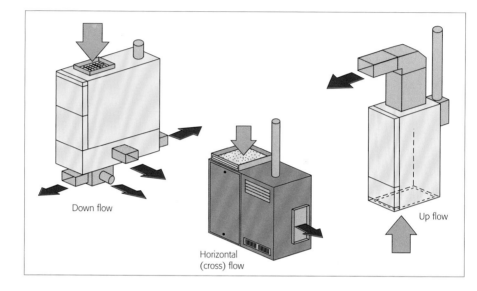

Down flow

Horizontal (cross) flow

Up flow

Figure 9.3 Typical downflow heater

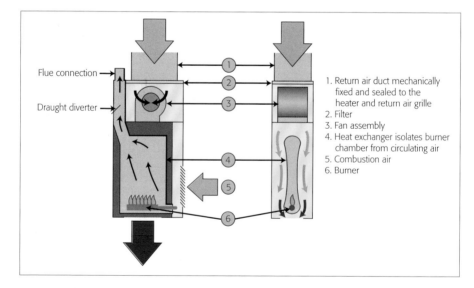

Flue connection

Draught diverter

1. Return air duct mechanically fixed and sealed to the heater and return air grille
2. Filter
3. Fan assembly
4. Heat exchanger isolates burner chamber from circulating air
5. Combustion air
6. Burner

Figure 9.4 Typical natural convection or brick central installation

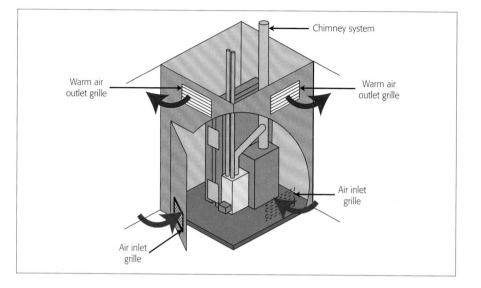

Fan assisted heaters are categorised with reference to the air flow movement through them and are generally divided into three main types (see Figure 9.2).

1. Up flow – generally free-standing, taking air from low level through a heat exchanger to discharge from high level ducting.

2. Down flow – generally free-standing, taking air from high level through a heat exchanger to discharge from low level ducting. This type is the most commonly used.

3. Horizontal (cross) flow – generally wall-mounted, taking air through a heat exchanger to discharge from side ducting.

Principle of operation

The air to be heated is drawn into the heater via the return air grille and through a filter or electronic cleaner (see **Return air (re-circulation) – Air filters for warm air heaters** in this Part). The air is fan-assisted to pass over a heat exchanger where its temperature is raised by 50°C ±5°C. The warm air enters a plenum (see **Warm air plenum** in this Part), which equalises the pressure and temperature before it is distributed into the dwelling via a network of ducts. Warm air enters the rooms/spaces through diffusers or registers fitted on the side wall, floor or ceiling. Displaced cooler air is then returned to the heater (see **Return air (re-circulation)** in this Part) for re-heating. A fan incorporated in the warm air heater provides the power for this circulation. Figure 9.3 shows the principle of operation of a typical down flow heater.

Note: Open-flued domestic warm air heaters have had a requirement since 1969 for a connection to be made from the return air spigot on the heater to the main return air grille(s). This positive return air connection prevents the circulation fan from interfering with the burner and an open-flue chimney system of the heater (see Return air (re-circulation) in this Part).

Natural convection model

Sometimes known as a 'Brick Central' model, air movement relies on natural convection to heat the dwelling. This type is not suitable for fan assisted ducted warm air.

The warm air heater is designed for installation in a convection chamber, which is located in the centre of the dwelling. This is a purpose-made compartment, constructed of brick, block or prefabricated panels.

Where a natural convection warm air heater has been specifically designed for siting in a convection chamber, the chamber should comply with the requirements for **Compartment installations** in this Part. Additionally, no air vent or duct should communicate directly between the chamber and any floor(s) sited above the chamber.

Principle of operation

Low level air inlet grilles allow cold air to enter the chamber, where it is warmed by the appliance heat exchanger. The warmed air is then discharged, by natural convection, through grilles or registers fitted at the top of the chamber (see Figure 9.4).

Due to the cooler air being heated by a heat exchanger, the appliance will generally not be fitted with an outer casing.

Conversion to another gas

Conversion to another gas, if necessary, should be carried out strictly in accordance with the appliance manufacturer's instructions and using their supplied kit of parts.

Restricted locations

Basements and cellars

An appliance fitted with an automatic means of ignition for use with LPG must not be installed in a room or internal space below ground level, e.g. a basement or cellar. This does not preclude the installation of such appliances into rooms which are basements with respect to one side of the building, but open to ground level on the opposite side.

Bath or shower rooms

Open-flue warm air heaters must not be installed in a room or internal space containing a bath or shower. This includes any cupboard/compartment or space (e.g. cubicle), which has an air path or connecting door opening into the bath or shower room. Only room-sealed appliances are suitable for installation and these locations should be considered only if there is no alternative.

Note: The above requirement applies to new installations. Existing open-flue warm air heaters, installed in such a location before 24th November 1984, may be serviced or repaired provided they are safe to use, but should be classed as Not to Current Standards (NCS) in line with the current Gas Industry Unsafe Situations Procedure (see also Essential Gas Safety – Domestic – Parts 8 and 10 for further guidance).

Bedroom/bedsitting rooms

Warm air heaters of greater than 14kW heat input (gross), installed in a room used or intended to be used as sleeping accommodation must be room-sealed. This includes any cupboard/compartment or space (e.g. cubicle), which has an air path or connecting door opening into the bedroom/bedsitting room.

Warm air heaters of 14kW heat input (gross) or less, may be room-sealed, or if open-flued, must incorporate a safety control designed to shut down the appliance before there is a dangerous quantity of POC in the room concerned. This device should be in the form of an atmosphere-sensing device (see **Part 13 Definitions**).

Note: These requirements apply to new installations including used or second-hand gas appliances installed after 1st January 1996. Existing appliances in these locations, provided they are safe to use, may be serviced or repaired but should be classed as Not to Current Standards (NCS) in line with the current Gas Industry Unsafe Situations Procedure (see also Essential Gas Safety – Domestic – Parts 8 and 10). The use of a fixed Carbon Monoxide detector Kite marked to BS EN 50291 may also be worth considering.

Covered passageways

Natural draught/fanned draught room-sealed and open-flued fanned draught flue terminals should not be sited within a covered passageway between properties e.g. terraced properties. In the case of room-sealed appliances, flues terminated in these positions may cause the POC to re-enter the air inlet duct, creating poor combustion at the burner. Flues terminated in these positions will produce POC, which could contain carbon monoxide (CO) and could accumulate entering habitable areas above the passageway.

Private garages

The Gas Safety (Installation and Use) Regulations 1984 banned the installation of open-flued appliances in private garages to reduce the risk of explosion/fire from hazardous substances such as petroleum vapour. This ban was relaxed on 31st October 1994. The Building Regulations in Scotland, which also placed certain restrictions on this type of installation, have also been relaxed and there is no longer a requirement for a gas appliance in a garage to be room-sealed.

If installing an open-flued warm air heater in a private garage, the appropriate regulations must be followed. It should be noted in addition that some manufacturers may not allow this type of installation.

Where gas operatives encounter open-flued warm air heaters already installed in a private garage, the customer should be advised to check their insurance policy, which may be affected by this type of installation.

Protected shafts/stairway

Protected shafts are stairs or other shafts passing directly from one compartment floor to another and are constructed and enclosed in such a way as to prevent the spread of fire or smoke.

An example of a protected shaft can often be found in flats over two storeys high, with individual accommodation on each floor, where the means of access and exit is via the protected stairway.

No gas appliances are permitted in a protected shaft/stairway.

Installation

Foreword

To avoid repetition, general information will be found in **Part 11 General installations details – Warm air systems**.

General

Warm air heaters can be installed in a number of ways. By far the most popular modern warm air heating appliance is the fan-assisted type. These guidance notes apply to fan assisted heaters and should be read in conjunction with the manufacturer's installation instructions.

At the initial planning stage consideration should be given to the following:

1. The size, type and location of the warm air heater should be noted. Adequate space should be allowed for the heater, its compartment or recess, plus the clearances and access space recommended by the manufacturer (N.B. by placing the heater centrally, duct runs can be kept short).

2. Associated ductwork (warm air and return air) system connections should be as short as possible. Short duct lengths increase efficiency and reduce costs. Wherever possible, the main return air duct should be taken from the hall or landing.

3. Warm air outlets (diffusers/registers) should be positioned to give optimum comfort levels.

4. The number of storeys in the building should be noted as this may determine additional requirements.

5. The chimney system type to be used should be noted (room-sealed or open-flued).

6. The location and/or route of the chimney system should be noted. For open-flued heaters, a simple vertical path will generally be suitable, as most heaters will be positioned centrally in the dwelling.

7. The ventilation requirements should be taken into consideration (see **Part 11 General installation details – Warm air systems – Ventilation**).

8. Availability of suitable gas and electric supplies should be considered.

9. Where applicable, the position of the domestic hot water storage vessel should be noted.

Types of buildings

Buildings of one or two storeys

Installation of warm air heaters in buildings of one or two storeys should be installed in accordance with the manufacturer's installation instructions.

Buildings of more than two storeys

Building Regulations specify additional requirements that should be complied with when a warm air heater is installed in any flat or maisonette, which has one of its floors, situated 4.5m or more above access level. This is because in the event of a fire, there is a possibility that a warm air heating system could allow smoke and fire from the dwelling to spread into a protected entrance hall or landing.

The following requirements also apply to any flat or maisonette in blocks of more than two storeys, with the exception of one and two storey dwellings, located within the blocks, which have their own access at ground level.

1. Air transfer grilles should not be fitted in any door, wall, floor or ceiling that communicates with a protected entrance hall or protected stairway.

2. All ductwork passing through any wall, floor or ceiling bounding a protected entrance hall or protected stairway should be fitted so that all joints between the ductwork and the boundary are fire stopped.

3. Where a duct conveys warm air into a protected entrance hall or protected stairway through any wall, floor or ceiling bounding the protected entrance hall or protected stairway, the return air from that area should be ducted back to the heater.

4. Warm air and return air grilles should be positioned at a height not exceeding 450mm above ground level to restrict the spread of smoke.

5. A room thermostat should be mounted in the living room at a height between 1370mm and 1830mm above floor level. Its maximum setting should not exceed 27°C.

Note: See also Restricted locations – Protected shafts/stairway in this Part.

Compartment installations

Warm air heaters may be installed in purpose-made compartments, which is probably the most commonly used installation method (see Figure 9.5). The compartment should comply with the following requirements:

1. It should be a fixed rigid construction.

2. Where the appliance manufacturer's installation instructions do not give specific advice, any internal surface of the compartment constructed of combustible material should be at least 75mm away from any part of the heater, alternatively, the surface should be lined with non-combustible material having a fire resistance of not less than 30 minutes. Materials that comply with the relevant part of BS 476 will generally meet these requirements.

3. It should be fitted with air vents at high and low level for the provision of compartment cooling and where an open-flue appliance is installed, combustion air should also be provided. The air vents should be sized in accordance with the manufacturer's instructions. See also the current British Standard for ventilation requirements: BS 5440-2 for further guidance.

4. An access door should be fitted to permit inspection, servicing and maintenance of the heater and any ancillary controls. The access door should be large enough to allow the heater to be removed.

5. To discourage its use as a storage cupboard, it should have a notice, fixed in a prominent position, to warn the customer against such use (see also Essential Gas Safety – Domestic – Part 10 for further guidance).

Figure 9.5 Typical compartment installations of a downflow fan-assisted ducted warm air heater

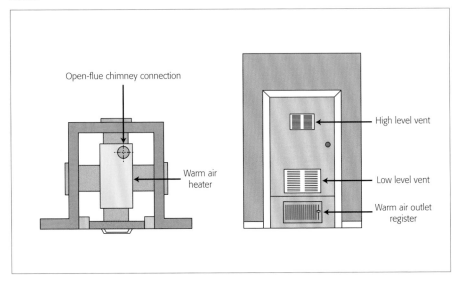

6. Where the heater is open-flued:

    • the return air grille should be connected directly to the appliance by means of a continuous duct (see **Return air (re-circulation)** in this Part)

    • the compartment door or air vents should not communicate with a room containing a bath or shower

    • for installations where the airing cupboard door or air vents communicate with a bedroom/bedsitting room (see **Bedroom/bedsitting rooms** in this Part)

    • air vents should not communicate with a garage.

7. Air vents should not penetrate a protected shaft or stairway (see **Restricted locations – Protected shafts/staiway** in this Part).

'Slot-fix' installations

'Slot-fix' installations are suitable for open-flue, low and moderate output heaters. They use little floor space and can be sited on the ground or first floor. The 'slot' protects both sides of the heater.

The 'slot-fix' type warm air heater is designed to be installed in a narrow recess with the front panel and controls exposed. Extra decorative panels fixed to the top of the heater fill in the opening to ceiling level in order to prevent the draught diverter and/or combustion air vents and/or return air grilles from being obstructed by the occupants of the dwelling. Combustion air enters the heater through the exposed panels or through special ventilation grilles incorporated into the design.

Figure 9.6 Slot-fix and free-standing/storey height installations

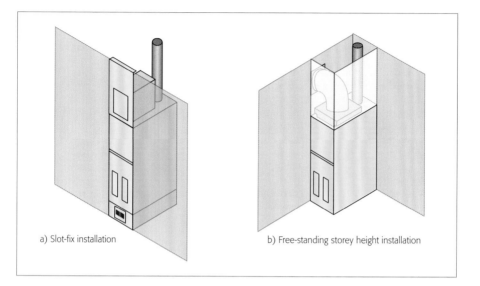

a) Slot-fix installation

b) Free-standing storey height installation

Note: Only appliances that are designed specifically for 'slot-fix' application can be fitted this way. Care should be taken to ensure adequate clearances from combustible materials. All installations should comply with the manufacturer's installation instructions (also see image 'a' in Figure 9.6).

Free-standing/storey height installations

In this situation, the warm air heater is installed in a room or hallway with at least one side (and preferably rear) against a wall (see image 'b' in Figure 9.6). A set of additional decorative panels extends the profile of the heater to ceiling level. Minimum floor space is used with these models. Generally the heater is on display, therefore its aesthetic appearance is important. Care when siting the heater is necessary to avoid transmission of sound from the heater fan. Care should also be taken to ensure adequate clearances from combustible materials.

Airing cupboard installations

When an airing cupboard is adapted to house a warm air heater the requirements given in **Compartment installations** in this Part should be followed. The airing cupboard door or air vents must not open into a bathroom or shower room, if the heater is open-flued.

For installations, where the airing cupboard door, or air vents communicate with a bedroom/bedsitting room (see **Bedroom/bedsitting rooms** in this Part).

Additionally, any other space(s) within the compartment should be separated from the heater by a non-combustible partition. If the partition is made of perforated material, the perforations should not exceed 13mm. This is to stop combustible material (e.g. clothes) from coming into contact with the heater or its chimney.

Where the heater is open-flued, the draught diverter and the air vents should be located within the heater space. The chimney system should be separated from the airing space with a non-combustible guard in order to prevent damage to the contents of the airing space.

Note: For double-wall flue pipe conforming to BS EN 1856-1, the level of insulation provided by the air gap between the outer and inner pipe may be deemed sufficient to provide the necessary protection. If the flue pipe is single-wall, a non-combustible guard should be fitted around the pipe, with a minimum of 25mm between the pipe and the guard. Clearances between the chimney guard and compartment partition should not exceed 13mm. Expanded metal or rigid wire mesh with apertures not exceeding 13mm are suitable materials for the partition and guard.

Understairs cupboard installations

When no practicable alternative location to site the heater is available an understairs installation may be considered. Whenever possible the heater should be room-sealed.

A warm air heater fitted in an understair cupboard or space should comply with the following requirements:

1. Where the premises in which the understairs cupboard is located is no more than two storeys, then the cupboard itself, should comply with the requirements given under **Compartment installations** in this Part.

2. Where the premises in which the heater is located is more than two storeys, all internal surfaces of the cupboard, including the base, should be constructed of materials that are non-combustible, or lined with non-combustible material (see Note).

3. The air vents should communicate direct to outside and should be sized in accordance with the manufacturer's instructions (see also the current British Standard for ventilation requirements: BS 5440-2 for further guidance).

Note: Non-combustible materials should have a fire resistance of not less than 30 minutes in accordance with the relevant part of BS 476.

Roof space installations

Warm air heaters installed in a roof space should be installed in accordance with the manufacturer's instructions. The general installation requirements are as follows:

1. A suitable flooring area capable of supporting the heater and any associated controls and equipment should be provided under and around the heater. If the flooring is of combustible material, a 12mm thick insulating base extending at least 25mm beyond the heater edges should be provided.

2. The heater should be accessible for service and maintenance.

3. A permanent means of access should be provided to the roof space (a fixed retractable roof ladder would be suitable).

4. A safety barrier should be provided around the roof space opening.

5. Fixed lighting should be provided for the heater and access area.

6. A safety barrier should be fitted around the heater to prevent contact with any stored items in the roof space.

7. If the heater is open-flued, adequate ventilation should be provided in the roof space.

Figure 9.7 Se-duct and U-duct installations

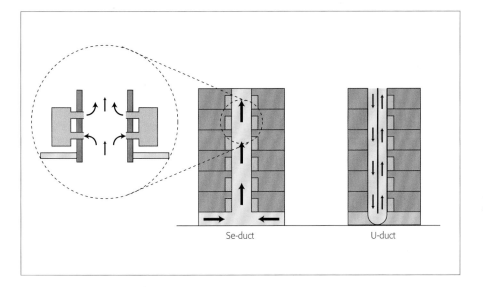

Se-duct   U-duct

Se-duct and U-duct appliance installations

Special room-sealed appliances are designed to suit the Se-duct and U-duct systems. Gas operatives should be sure that the appliance is suitable for the purpose before commencing installation.

Se-duct and U-ducts are shared chimney systems generally built into blocks of flats, usually high rise. Combustion air is taken from the shared chimney and POC are channelled back into the shared chimney system.

Se-ducts are designed so that the chimney system is open to atmosphere at both ends, allowing airflow through the duct. The air inlets (of which there is often more than one per duct) are positioned at low level and the termination or exhaust (of which there is only one per duct) at high level.

U-ducts are similar to Se-ducts in their function. The duct is arranged in a 'U' shape with both the air entry and termination (or exhaust) open to atmosphere on the top of the building. The inlet and outlet spigots of the appliances are connected to the up-flow leg of the system.

Special room-sealed appliances are installed against the ducts and connected to it by two open spigots in accordance with manufacturer's instructions. Each warm air heater takes in combustion air via its bottom spigot, which is normally flush with the Se/U-duct inner wall. The POC are discharged back into the same duct through the longer upper spigot (see Figure 9.7).

The warm air heater is generally fitted in a compartment. Construction and ventilation requirements are as described under **Compartment installations** in this Part.

Return air (re-circulation)

Introduction

It has been a requirement in Building Regulations, since 1969, for domestic open-flued warm air heaters to be fitted with a full and unobstructed return air arrangement. This is to prevent the circulation fan from interfering with the burner and chimney system of the heater. A positive return air connection should be made between the return air spigot on the heater and the main return air grille(s). Before 1969, a positive return air system was only required where the warm air heater had a heat output exceeding 7kW.

This requirement applies directly to open-flued appliances installed in a compartment and will also apply to 'slot fix' and free standing storey height installations. In general terms, however, to ensure a safe installation, it is recommended that open-flued domestic installations in all situations/locations, a positive return air connection should be made between the return air spigot on the heater and the main return air grille(s).

Where an existing domestic open-flued warm air heater with fanned warm air circulation is encountered, that does not have a positive return air arrangement, then when ever possible/practicable a positive return air connection should be made/recommended. Before any remedial work is undertaken, the appliance manufacturers should be consulted for the particular requirements for each appliance type.

Attention: With regard to existing installations, where there is no positive return air connection, the installation should be classed as At Risk (AR) in accordance with the current Gas Industry Unsafe Situations Procedure (see also Essential Gas Safety – Domestic – Parts 8 and 10 for further guidance).

Where, however, there is no provision on the appliance to install a positive return air connection, then advice should be sought from the appliance manufacturer, or other warm air specialist.

A full and unobstructed return air path should be provided to the heater from all heated rooms and spaces, with the exception of kitchens, bathrooms and toilets. This allows air from heated rooms/spaces to be returned (transferred) to the heater for re-heating and re-circulation. The return air path itself, is provided by return air grilles connected by ducts to the heater. Air relief openings allow air to move to the return air grilles from other rooms/spaces, but these should not be fitted directly between bedrooms. The chimney system should not run through an area serving as a return air path.

When warm air heaters are installed in any house, flat or maisonette, which has one of its floors, situated 4.5m or more above access level, there are additional requirements with which gas operatives should comply. These additional requirements apply to all dwellings in blocks of more than two storeys, with the exception of one and two storey dwellings located within the blocks that have their own access at ground level (see **Types of buildings – Buildings of more than two storeys** in this Part).

Figure 9.8 Air relief openings

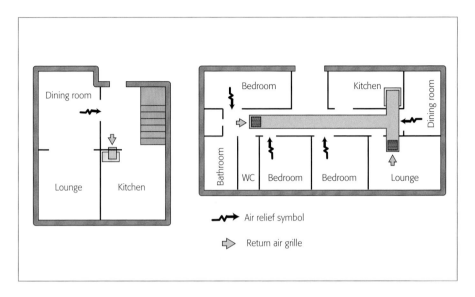

Return air grilles

Ideally, return air grilles are best positioned in hallways, landings or in another suitable 'collection area' within easy location of the warm air heater see Figure 9.8. The grille(s) should be connected to the heater by a duct. The collection area may have air relief openings from other heated rooms/spaces. In smaller dwellings a single return air grille will be required. However, in larger dwellings several return air grilles may be required for each floor or area. If more than one return air grille is fitted, all grilles should be connected directly to the heater by using the same duct see Figure 9.8.

Where a living room is used as the collection area, care should be taken when positioning the return air grille to ensure that the cooler air moving from other rooms does not create draughts. Larger rooms may benefit from an additional return air grille serving only that room.

Note: A collection area is where all heated rooms/spaces are connected to one area by means of a number of air relief openings.

Air relief (or transfer) openings

Air relief openings depend generally on the construction and layout of the dwelling (see Figure 9.8).

They should be fitted in all heated rooms except kitchens, bathrooms and toilets to provide a path to the collection area. Openings can be in doors or walls but should not be subject to accidental blockage. Therefore, gaps under doors are not acceptable. A grille should cover the openings.

Positioning of return air grilles/air relief openings

Return air grilles and air relief openings are designed to circulate the air within the room and return the cooler air back to the heater. The following points should be considered when deciding their positions:

1. Providing there is no alternative, a living room may be used as a 'collection area', but care should be taken to locate return air grilles and relief air openings, to ensure that cooler air returning from other parts of the building does not create draughts.

2. Return air grilles should preferably not be positioned in a room containing an open-flued appliance (this includes solid fuel, oil and gas appliance types). Where this is unavoidable, the inlet velocity should not exceed 1.5m/s and any air relief opening to the living room sized correctly (see Attention).

3. Unless advised by the appliance manufacturer, return air grilles may be sited at high or low level in walls, ceilings or floors (see also **Types of buildings** in this Part).

4. If the warm air distribution supply register/diffuser is at one end, the return air grille or air relief opening should be positioned at the opposite end of the room, particularly in long narrow rooms.

5. Grilles should be positioned at low level, if warm air is supplied at high level and vice versa.

6. Grilles should not be sited adjacent to warm air outlets (may cause the heater to cycle more frequently).

7. Avoid siting low level grilles in a likely sitting area (occupants may suffer from cold ankles).

Attention: Failure to make the necessary allowances for return air grilles/air relief openings, could in the case of a room in which a return air grille is sited and from which return air is taken, to subject that room to sub-atmospheric pressure (caused by the suction of the warm air circulation fan). This could adversely affect the safe operation of the warm air heater itself and/or any other open-flued appliance in the same or adjoining rooms.

Return air ducting

Open-flued appliances

The main return air grille(s) should be positioned in a suitable 'collection area', e.g. a hall or landing. For ease of installation they are generally fitted in a wall or a ceiling. A duct should be connected from the return air grille(s) to the return air inlet on the appliance. Manufacturers have made it easier to install this positive return air link, by designing appliances that have a choice of top and side return air connections.

The duct should be sealed so that the return air is separated from the combustion air within the heater compartment, or heater case. If this is not sealed, this could adversely affect the safe operation of the chimney system. The optimum method is to use a rigid metal duct (see Figure 9.9), or flexible return air kits are available which are simple to fit (see Figure 9.10). It is important that the duct is correctly fixed and secured with screws or rivets to the wall/ceiling/heater and sealed. Where a flexible duct kit is used it may be necessary to connect it to the square or rectangular return air connection on the heater. An adaptor for this purpose may be obtained from the warm air heater manufacturer.

Note: Care should be taken to ensure that the flexible ducting does not come into contact with the hot surfaces of the chimney system or draught diverter of the warm air heater.

Return air ducts should be designed to avoid transmission of noise from the warm air heater fan compartment. This is particularly important when return air grilles are sited in living rooms or where the heater has a relatively high fan speed.

To avoid this, short return air ducts should not be used. Alternatively, at least one bend should be incorporated in the duct. If this cannot be achieved, short duct lengths should be lined with a sound absorbing material.

Sizing of air relief openings/return air grilles/return air ducts

Return air grilles and air relief openings should be sized to handle air equal in volume to the warm air supplied to the rooms/areas they serve. They are sized similarly for open-flued or room-sealed appliances. The velocity of air through the grilles should not exceed 2m/s.

Relief air openings should have a free area of 88cm^2/kW of heat input to a room/space.

A guide to sizing return air grilles and return air ducts can be found in Table 9.2. It is based on typical grilles with a free area of 70% of the total grille size, which is a general manufacturing design. For grilles with different free areas, consult the manufacturer's data.

Attention: The importance of providing correctly sized return air grilles/air relief (or transfer) openings should not be underestimated. Failure to make the necessary allowances for return air grilles/air relief openings, could in the case of a room in which a return air grille is sited and from which return air is taken, subject that room to sub-atmospheric pressure (caused by the suction of the warm air circulation fan). This could adversely affect the safe operation of the warm air heater itself and/or any other open-flued appliance in the same or adjoining rooms.

Care should be taken to ensure that in all instances where open-flued heaters are installed, that a spillage test is carried out on the heater chimney system, to ensure that there is no spillage of POC taking place caused by the operation of the warm air circulation fan.

In cases where spillage is detected, calculations should be checked/re-checked to ensure that there is an adequately sized return air path back to the heater. In the case of an open-flued heater installed in a location other than a compartment, e.g. a room, it may be necessary to install a positive return air connection between the return air spigot on the heater and the main return air grille(s) into the room.

Figure 9.9 Rigid metal return air duct

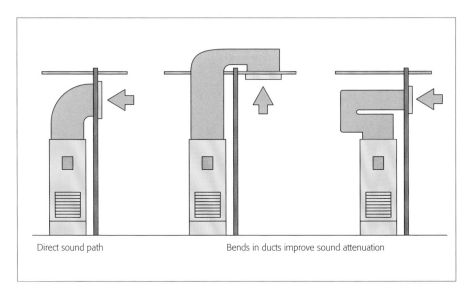

Direct sound path   Bends in ducts improve sound attenuation

Figure 9.10 Flexible return air connection

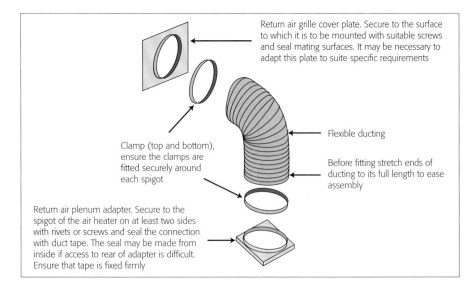

Return air grille cover plate. Secure to the surface to which it is to be mounted with suitable screws and seal mating surfaces. It may be necessary to adapt this plate to suite specific requirements

Flexible ducting

Before fitting stretch ends of ducting to its full length to ease assembly

Clamp (top and bottom), ensure the clamps are fitted securely around each spigot

Return air plenum adapter. Secure to the spigot of the air heater on at least two sides with rivets or screws and seal the connection with duct tape. The seal may be made from inside if access to rear of adapter is difficult. Ensure that tape is fixed firmly

Table 9.2 Return air grille/duct sizing

Output up to kW	Return air grille size (mm)	Return air duct size Rigid (mm)	Return air duct size Flexible (mm)
7.5	350 x 250	200 x 200	250 diameter
8.8	350 x 300	250 x 200	250 diameter
10.3	350 x 350	250 x 250	300 diameter
11.7	400 x 350	250 x 250	300 diameter
13.2	400 x 400	300 x 250	300 diameter
14.7	450 x 400	300 x 250	300 diameter
17.6	450 x 450	300 x 300	350 diameter
19.1	500 x 450	350 x 300	400 diameter

Room-sealed appliances

Room-sealed appliances may be installed without a duct connecting the return air grille(s) to the return air inlet on the appliance, providing that there is a return path to the heater. It is essential that the cooler air from other heated rooms returning to the collection area has an unobstructed return air path to the heater.

Air filters for warm air heaters

Air filters come in a range of designs and materials and are located in the appliance to filter the incoming air returning to the appliance. Generally these are:

1. A glass fibre blanket material, which is placed over an open cage in the form of a 'hammock' to present a large area to the incoming return air. Used in both up-flow and down-flow heaters.

2. A fine plastic mesh, which is held in place within a ridged frame and allows for easy removal and cleaning. Often used in slot-fix appliances.

3. Electrostatic/electronic air filtration – A method where even minute dust particles, tobacco smoke, pollen and other atmospheric pollutants are removed from the air by polarising the filter medium with an electrostatic charge, making this an ideal method of filtration for those persons who suffer from air borne allergies.

Generally, air filters should be removed and cleaned every two weeks during the heating season.

Figure 9.11 Warm air plenum

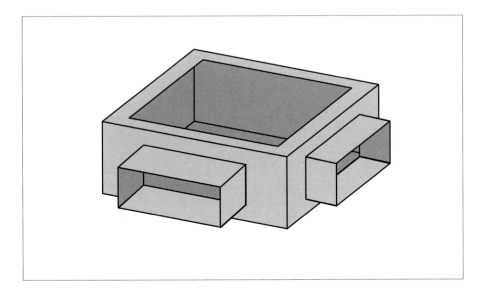

Duct systems

Introduction

The following guidance is based on the use of galvanised steel ductwork, which is the most commonly used. Any other material used to construct the ductwork will require individual consideration as to its suitability in relation to fire resistance and airflow.

Duct layouts and sizes are determined by their length and the volume of air (heat), which they carry. The most important factor to consider is the resistance to airflow.

The following guidelines should be followed:

1. Use the least number of duct fittings, i.e. bends and tee's.

2. Select components of low resistance (high resistance components e.g. square bends without internal air guides, or sudden changes in the duct cross-sectional area, should be avoided).

3. Always use take-off fittings (branch ducts) that are angled in the direction of the airflow.

4. Position take-off fittings or branches on straight sections of the main duct. They should not be connected to elbows, bends or transition fittings.

Warm air plenum

A warm air plenum is a 'box' designed to equalise air pressure to the supply ducts (see Figure 9.11). It is designed to be connected to the warm air heater outlet. The plenum will be designed with a number of 'take-off' duct connections on the side to allow heating ducts to be connected. Where possible, the duct connections should not face the airflow from the heater outlet.

Warm air plenums used with down-flow heaters are designed to stand on the floor and should be constructed to support the total weight of the heater (these are known as base or duct plenums). Up-flow and horizontal (cross) flow plenums are similarly constructed but are not weight bearing.

Attention: When installing open-flued warm air heaters it is imperative to check that the joint between the heater and the plenum base is adequately sealed. Any discharge of air through inadequate sealing between the heater and plenum may have a detrimental affect on combustion and adversely affect chimney operation. The same checks should also be made to both ductwork connections and blanked off outlets of the plenum to ensure that they are adequately sealed. All joints should be mechanically sealed/secured e.g. by self-tapping screws or by pop rivets. Duct tape is not for securing.

Failure to ensure this could result in the combustion becoming vitiated, creating poor combustion, resulting in the production of carbon monoxide (CO).

In addition it is important that:

1. The heater is firmly supported; and

2. There is a 100% air path between the opening in the base of the heater and the plenum or base duct.

Balancing dampers

Ideally, warm air systems should be designed so that the main duct runs are in balance, i.e. so that they have the same resistance to the airflow that they are designed to handle.

This degree of balance is not always possible (due to standard size ducts), therefore, 'balancing dampers' may have to be included in the system design to reduce the air velocity. If, for example, a system has mostly long duct runs but includes one very short one, a damper should be included in the short run to balance the system. Air velocity in rising ducts increases significantly. A damper may therefore have to be included. Dampers can be positioned in the ducts or immediately behind registers or diffusers (see Figure 9.12).

Types of duct systems

In most duct systems the cross-sectional area of a duct is kept roughly proportional to the volume of air passing through any point. The size of the duct should therefore reduce as it branches. Normally one size is used for the main duct with the branches reducing in size as necessary.

Air velocities in ducts should not exceed 4m/s. Typical ranges of duct size for which standard components and fittings are commonly used are shown in Tables 9.3 and 9.4.

The type of duct system fitted will have to meet the needs of a wide variety of residential installations, with the final choice depending on the building layout and economics. It may include more than one design to serve different floors/areas of a dwelling. Generally, the type of duct system will be one of the following three designs, stepped duct system, extended plenum system or radial (or stub duct) system.

Figure 9.12 Types of dampers

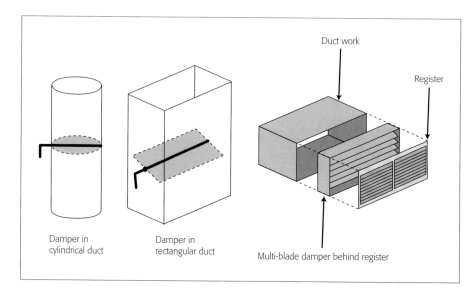

Duct work

Register

Damper in
cylindrical duct

Damper in
rectangular duct

Multi-blade damper behind register

Table 9.3 Typical duct sizes – cylindrical

Cylindrical duct (mm)
100
125
150
175

Table 9.4 Typical duct sizes – rectangular

Rectangle duct (mm)	
150 x 100	200 x 200
150 x 200	200 x 300
150 x 250	200 x 400
150 x 300	200 x 500
150 x 350	200 x 600

Figure 9.13 Stepped duct system

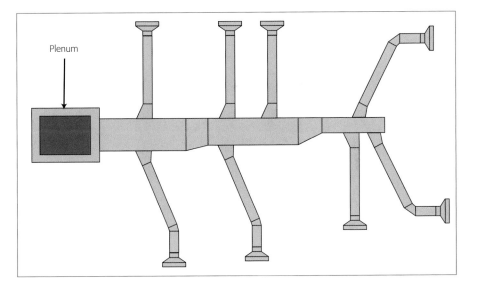

Plenum

Stepped duct system

This consists of a main rectangular duct, with individual branches of either round or rectangular ducts. Figure 9.13 shows one main duct extending from the warm air plenum, but in practice there could be two or more main ducts either connected to the warm air plenum or branching from the main duct to form other main ducts. Take-off fittings from main ducts to individual areas of the dwelling should be slanted in the direction of the airflow from the heater. Reducing fittings are used where cross-sectional area changes are required.

Extended plenum system

This is a simplified duct system where the main rectangular duct is the same size throughout its length, extending the warm air plenum (see Figures 9.14 and 9.15). Smaller round or rectangular ducts extend the system into individual areas of the dwelling.

This system can provide full perimeter heating and is best installed as part of the building structure.

The extended plenum system has two basic rules of conformity:

- main duct(s) should be no longer than 6m

- branch ducts should be no longer than 6m and contain no more than two bends (excluding boots)

Note: A boot is the transition from the round or rectangular duct to the diffuser/register (see Figure 9.16).

Figure 9.14 Extended plenum system

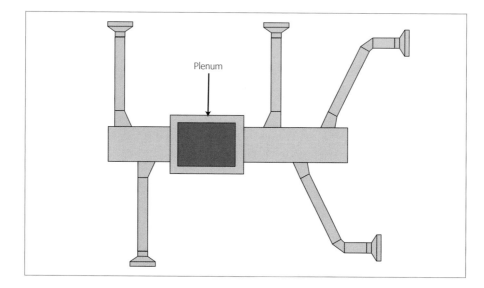

Figure 9.15 Extended plenum system (perimeter)

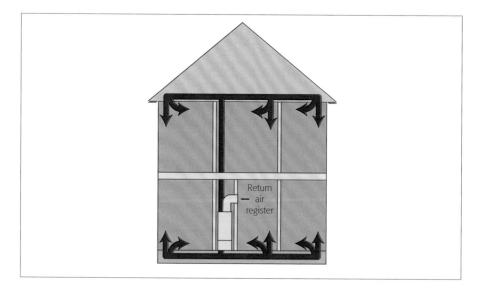

Figure 9.16 Boot fittings

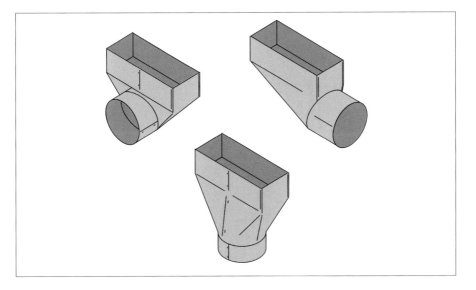

Figure 9.17 Radial system

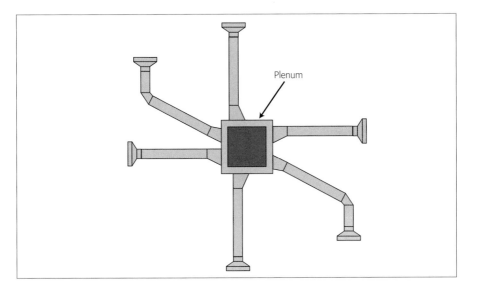

Figure 9.18 Low sidewall (stub duct) system

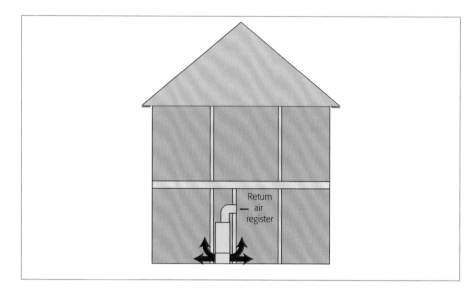

Radial (or Stub duct) system

This system may also be known as a Low Sidewall (Stub duct) system. It can be less labour intensive as it can be installed without under-floor ducts. The warm air heater is centrally located with low sidewall registers to the living room, kitchen and hall. It can be extended to give similar heating to the first floor.

Cylindrical or rectangular ducts branch directly from the warm air plenum to individual areas of the dwelling. Figures 9.17 and 9.18 are examples of their application.

This type of system has a basic rule of conformity:

*   branch ducts should be no longer than 6m and contain no more than two bends (excluding boots)

Balancing the heating system

Introduction

Balancing is carried out to ensure that heat is discharged in the various rooms/spaces according to their requirements. Systems that are out of balance may not give the required comfort conditions. Some rooms/spaces may be too hot or too cold, whilst others are correctly heated. Balancing involves adjusting the flow of air and it can be carried out in both warm or cold weather.

A deflection type anemometer is recommended for recording the air velocity, as this will automatically adjust for changes in air density due to temperature changes.

An accurate thermometer capable of reading at least 70°C will also be required.

Some problems may be encountered due to duct lengths causing differing resistances, for example:

1. Very short duct runs, or registers fitted directly to the warm air plenum or base duct generally have a low resistance to air flow. However, when installed together with some extended duct runs, which themselves have a high resistance, this creates an imbalance. This can be overcome by installing multi-blade dampers behind registers in short (low resistance) ducts to increase their resistance.

2. Overheating of rooms upstairs rooms may be caused by too little resistance in ducts. This can be overcome by installing an adjustable damper in the rising duct(s) to increase resistance.

Balancing procedure

It is unlikely that any two air measuring instruments will indicate the same reading for a constant velocity. It is not therefore possible to set velocities to specific design figures if readings cannot be accepted as being accurate by the measuring instrument used.

Design velocities should be considered to be 'guide velocities'. By using the following procedure, it is possible to obtain a satisfactory system balance by setting velocities in correct proportions.

Table 9.5 shows the Air velocity factors.

Table 9.6 shows the Guide balancing velocities.

Table 9.7 shows the Final balancing velocities.

1. On warm air heaters with modulating controls, set the air circulation fan at maximum speed. Some warm air heaters with modulating controls (even temperature (ET) systems) have a switch labelled 'continuous' for this purpose. On basic models (those without an ET system) it will be necessary to bypass the fan switch as it does not allow the fan to operate if no heat is detected. This should be carried out following manufacturer's instructions.

2. Carry out the measurements with the electrical supply ON but the main burner OFF.

3. Partly close the balancing dampers of the diffuser/registers nearest to the warm air heater, and fully open those furthest away.

4. A worked example is shown in Tables 9.6 and 9.7 (see Note).

Note: For a genuine application, the heat required would be as given in the actual design and specification being installed. Air velocity factors in Table 9.6 are obtained from Table 9.5.

5. Establish the design balancing velocities from Table 9.6 and enter them in column 'A' of Table 9.7.

6. Measure the actual air velocity at each outlet and enter them in column 'B' of Table 9.7. Start at the diffuser/register nearest the heater and work away until the outlet on the longest duct is measured.

7. For each diffuser/register, divide the measured velocity by the design velocity (column 'B' divided by column 'A') and enter results in column 'C' of Table 9.7.

8. Find the average of column 'C' (add the results together and divide by the number of diffusers/registers) and note in column 'C' of Table 9.7.

Table 9.5 Air velocity factors

Register size (mm x mm)	Air velocity factor
150 x 100	87
200 x 100	67
200 x 150	44
250 x 150	35
250 x 200	26
300 x 150	30
300 x 200	22
Diffuser size (mm x mm)	**Air velocity factor**
57 x 250	93
57 x 300	78
57 x 350	67
100 x 250	53
100 x 300	44

Table 9.6 Guide balancing velocities (figures shown are an example)

Room Column 1	Heat required (kW) Column 2	Register size (mm) Column 3	Air velocity factor Column 4	Guide velocity (Column 2 x Column 4) x 0.017 gives metres per second (m/s)
Lounge	2.5	250 x 150	35	1.49
Kitchen	1.3	200 x 100	67	1.48
Hall	1.5	200 x 150	44	1.12
Bathroom	0.9	200 x 100	67	1.03
Bedroom	1.9	200 x 150	44	1.42

Table 9.7 Final balancing velocities in m/s (figures shown are an example)

Warm Air Outlet	Room	Guide Design Balancing Velocities (m/s) Column A	Measured Velocities (Assumed) (m/s) Column B	Column B ÷ Column A Column C	Balancing Velocities (m/s) Column A x Average of Column C Column D
1	Lounge	1.49	1.4	0.94	(1.49 x 1.11) = **1.66**
2	Kitchen	1.48	1.3	0.88	(1.48 x 1.11) = **1.65**
3	Hall	1.12	1.6	1.43	(1.12 x 1.11) = **1.24**
4	Bathroom	1.03	1.3	1.26	(1.03 x 1.11) = **1.14**
5	Bedroom	1.42	1.5	1.06	(1.42 x 1.11) = **1.58**
				Total = 5.57	
				Average = 5.57 ÷ 5	
				= **1.11**	

9. Finally, multiply each design guide velocity in column 'A' by the average in column 'C' and enter results in column 'D' of Table 9.7.

10. Balance the system to the figures in column 'D' of Table 9.7 by adjusting the dampers and registers as necessary.

Following the balancing process, if the warm air heater has modulating controls (ET system) switch from 'continuous' to allow the fan speed control to operate and complete commissioning as described in the manufacturer's instructions.

On basic models (those without an ET system), re-establish the fan switch and adjust the fan speed, to give a temperature rise across the heater, which is close to the design value and complete commissioning as described in the manufacturer's instructions.

If the temperature rise across the heater when measured is under or over 6°C of the design figure, adjust the fan speed to alter the temperature rise to the design figure.

Note: The temperature rise across the heater is taken as the difference between the return air temperature (measured at the air filter) and the supply temperature measured as close as possible to the heater (i.e. at the nearest air diffuser/register to the heater).

If necessary, the supply air temperature can be altered by adjusting the fan speed.

Where diffusers/registers have dampers, which have their travel distance limited by adjusting screws, adjust these to the maximum limit at the settings used.

Finally, adjust the vanes on the diffusers/registers to give the desired direction of warm air flow. The system should stay ' in balance' unless interfered with by others.

Warm air heater replacement – 10

10 – Warm air heater replacement

Figures

Introduction

It is important when planning the replacement of a warm air heater that the new installation conforms to the current Gas Safety (Installation and Use) Regulations, the appliance manufacturer's instructions and current British standards. Reference should also be made to the installation guidelines of **Warm air heating** in Part 9 of this manual.

This guidance generally applies to the replacement of open-flued gas-fired warm air heaters in domestic premises of one or two storeys. Buildings of more than two storeys have additional requirements (see **Part 9 Warm air heating – Types of buildings**).

For commissioning, servicing, maintenance and fault finding procedures see **Part 11 General installation details – Warm air systems**.

Warm air heating systems were at their most popular in the 1960s and 1970s and were installed to the British Standards in force at the time. Many of these installations may now be due for replacement and upgrading to current installation standards.

The first point to consider when replacing a warm air heating installation is to determine whether the design of the existing system is satisfactory. This can be achieved by asking the user whether the existing system is providing the required amount of heat to the rooms or internal spaces (hall, landing etc.). Depending on the user's reaction, the heating system may need to be totally re-designed or it may simply require balancing correctly to meet their requirements, once the new heater is installed.

Some older types of warm air heaters are controlled by a room thermostat, which operates the main burner and circulation fan as soon as heat is called for, causing cold air to be delivered until the heat exchanger is up to temperature. When satisfied, the room thermostat shuts down the burner and circulation fan together, leaving a residue of heat in the heater. The introduction of the fan delay switch greatly improved comfort levels by delaying the circulation fan operation until heat was available. Also, the circulation fan runs on after the burner has switched off, distributing all residual heat within the heater. Further developments have seen the introduction of Even Temperature (ET) systems that modulate both the burner output and circulation fan speed by constantly sensing heat requirements.

Some problems with existing systems can be simply overcome by carrying out a service on the appliance (see **Part 11 General installation details – Warm air systems – Servicing**), or it may be a case of replacing a very old appliance and re-using the existing ductwork system, in which case the following points should be considered:

1. Warm air registers may have been fitted incorrectly, so that the closeable vanes are directing warm air upwards instead of downwards. The user removing the register to decorate and re-fitting it the wrong way round may have caused this.

2. Balancing dampers (see **Part 9 Warm air heating – Duct systems – Balancing dampers**) may not have been fitted at the time of installation to allow the system to be correctly balanced. It is not uncommon to find house bricks placed in ducts (by the original commissioning engineer or builder installing the ducts) for the purpose of balancing.

3. Draughts may be experienced due to air velocity at registers being too high.

4. Ducts and registers may have been undersized and therefore, incapable of delivering sufficient heat.

5. Some parts of the room/space may be too cold due to badly positioned warm air outlets causing poor warm air circulation.

Choosing the right heater

Before choosing the replacement heater it is important to assess the existing system and to know whether the new system is to be extended to other unheated parts of the dwelling. The requirement should take into account the following points:

1. Heat requirements – heat loss calculations for each room/space to be heated should be carried out to determine the heater size (see **Part 9 Warm air heating – Design of warm air systems**).

2. Duct system – an inspection of the existing duct system should be made to ensure that it is in good condition and sized correctly for the heat requirements (see **Part 9 Warm air heating – Duct systems**).

3. Registers/diffusers – these should be correctly sized for the heat requirements and operate satisfactorily.

If the existing system is to be utilised, deciding which replacement heater to install depends largely upon the existing position and condition of the following major components of the installation:

- warm air plenum
- type of air flow (upflow, downflow or horizontal (cross) flow)
- type of flue connection on existing heater e.g. front or rear
- chimney system
- return air arrangement
- water heating requirements

Warm air plenum

The prime objective when replacing a warm air heater is to ensure that any leakage of air from the existing plenum and ductwork system is kept to a minimum. This is especially important where the heater is fitted in a compartment. It is of paramount importance that the circulation fan of the heater is prevented from interfering with the operation of the burner and the chimney system. All existing ductwork joints should be thoroughly examined and where necessary made mechanically sound i.e. by using self-tapping screws/pop rivets and finally sealed with duct tape. The existing plenum should be in good, sound condition if it is to be re-used. Consideration should be given to replacing the plenum.

The warm air plenum is a 'box' designed to equalise air pressure and temperature before it is distributed into the dwelling through a network of ducts connected to it.

Figure 10.1 Fitting new heater to existing plenum

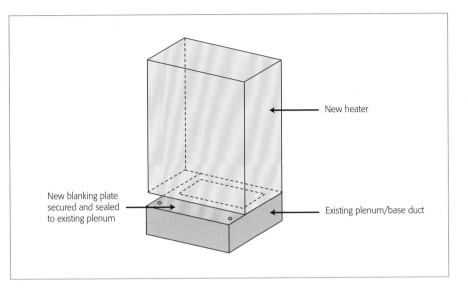

New heater

New blanking plate secured and sealed to existing plenum

Existing plenum/base duct

The gas operative will need to identify the heater type, either upflow, downflow or horizontal (cross) flow (see **Part 9 Warm air heating – Types and application of heaters**). The heater type will determine the position and construction of the plenum. Warm air plenums used with downflow type heaters are designed to allow the heater to stand directly on them and they should be constructed to support the weight of the heater. Upflow and horizontal (cross) flow heater plenums are similarly constructed but are not weight-carrying.

Modern warm air heaters differ in dimensions to older types and are generally smaller. If re-using the existing plenum, it may therefore require adapting to fit the new heater and it may be necessary to blank off openings left by the old heater (see Figure 10.1). It is recommended that the warm air heater manufacturer's adapter kit, which contains specific instructions on how to fit and secure it to the existing plenum, be used. The blanking plate should be secured mechanically to the plenum i.e. with self-tapping screws or pop rivets, and sealed using a self adhesive foam strip, Neoprene sealing strip, or a suitable sealing compound (see Note).

Note: Duct tape is for sealing not for securing.

When installing open-flued warm air heaters, any discharge of air through inadequate sealing between the new heater and the existing plenum may have a detrimental effect on combustion and chimney performance. It is therefore extremely important that an effective seal is made between the heater and the plenum.

In addition, it is important that:

1. The new heater is firmly supported; and

2. There is a 100% air path between the opening in the base of the new heater and the existing plenum or base duct.

Type of air flow

Fan-assisted heaters are categorised with reference to the air flow movement through them and are generally divided into three types (see **Part 9 Warm air heating – Figure 9.2**):

1. Upflow – generally free-standing, taking air from low level through a heat exchanger, to discharge to high level ducting.

2. Downflow – generally free-standing, taking air from high level through a heat exchanger to discharge to low level ducting. This type is the most commonly used.

3. Horizontal (cross) flow – generally wall-mounted, taking air through a heat exchanger to discharge to side ducting.

Note: If the replacement heater has a different type of airflow than the existing one, major alterations to the duct system may have to be carried out.

Type of open-flue chimney connection

Once installed, the replacement heater should be correctly flued. Heaters are designed with chimney connections that are located either at the back, top rear or top front (see **Part 9 Warm air heating – Figure 9.1**). If the replacement heater does not have a similar chimney connection, alterations will need to be made, which may affect the chimney performance. Excessive use of chimney bends should be avoided, so it is important that the new heater's chimney connection is similar to the existing one.

Chimney system – open-flue

General

Warm air heating system efficiency relies on short ductwork runs. Most warm air heaters are therefore generally positioned in the centre of the dwelling. A typical existing chimney system normally runs from the heater up through a bedroom and into the loft area, terminating to atmosphere with a ridge terminal. Alternatively, it may pass directly through the pitched/flat roof terminating with an approved terminal.

When replacing the old heater with a new one, the chimney system requires particular attention as it may involve:

1. Connecting to the existing chimney system; or

2. Complete renewal of the chimney system.

Whichever option is selected the chimney system should ultimately conform to the warm air heater manufacturer's installation instructions (see also Essential Gas Safety – Domestic – Part 13 for further guidance).

Connecting to an existing asbestos cement chimney system

Many early open-flued warm air heaters were flued using asbestos cement flue pipe and fittings. Where this material is encountered, providing that the following basic checks are carried out beforehand, this type of chimney system may be re-used:

1. Only one appliance should be connected to the chimney system.

2. Check the entire route of the chimney to ensure that:

   a) There are no bends in the chimney greater than 45 degrees to the vertical which could adversely affect the performance of the chimney or result in a blockage.

   b) All joints are inspected and made good where necessary.

   c) The chimney is correctly supported.

   d) The chimney is in good condition for re-use.

3. The termination should be examined and replaced as necessary. Older ridge terminal adapters ('R' type adapters), which provide the connection between flue pipe and ridge terminal, (see Figure 10.2) are known to have securing bolts that are subject to corrosion. Check their security/suitability to ensure that they are fit for further use. In the past, some securing bolts were manufactured using plastic materials. These also should be replaced.

4. Where an old type ridge terminal is fitted, these are known to have a high flow resistance. Consideration should be given to the fitting of a new, less restrictive type (see Figure 10.3).

High flow resistance ridge terminals are typically open on two sides (front and back) and generally follow the profile of the ridge tiles. Whereas low flow resistance ridge terminals are generally open on all four sides and project above the profile of the ridge tiles.

Existing chimney systems that do not comply with current standards, or are in poor condition should be upgraded. This is generally achieved by connecting double-walled metallic flue pipe/fittings to the 'sound' part of the existing asbestos cement chimney system.

Special fittings are normally available from chimney system manufacturers to connect to the existing asbestos cement chimney. This method generally uses a socket type fitting that requires a flue-jointing compound applied to the connection of the existing chimney. Gas operatives should note that using excessive flue jointing compound may force some of the compound out of the joint and into the flue pipe. This could obstruct and thereby reduce the internal diameter of the chimney pipe.

Warning: Asbestos removal is specialist work and should only be carried out by approved businesses as defined in the Control of Asbestos at Work Regulations. In accordance with the Health and Safety at Work etc. Act, special safety precautions should be applied when working on an existing asbestos cement flue pipe/fitting. For further advice, contact the Health and Safety Executive Information line on 08701 545 500.

Figure 10.2 Ridge terminal adapter ('R' type adapter)

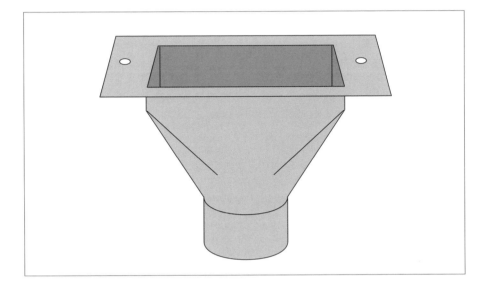

Figure 10.3 Typical low resistance ridge terminations

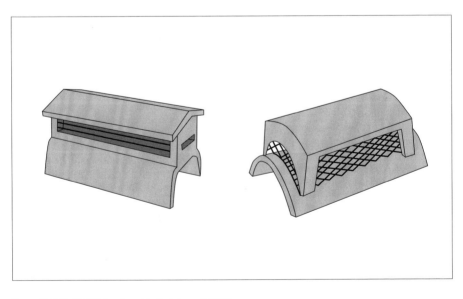

Note: When connecting to an existing chimney or part-renewing the chimney system, the removal of the existing warm air heater will cause some movement, however small, of the existing chimney system. On completion of the installation of the replacement heater items 2 b) c) d) and 3 of Connecting to an existing asbestos cement chimney system should be carried out again.

Connecting to an existing lined chimney system

If connecting to a flexible metallic liner, the existing liner should be replaced unless it is considered that it will continue to operate safely throughout the life span of the new warm air heater. Under normal operating conditions, a liner complying with BS EN 1856-2 should operate safely for at least the operational life span of an appliance, (normally 10-15 years). Therefore, if the existing warm air heater is in excess of 10 years old, it is recommended that the liner be replaced.

Connecting to an existing twin walled chimney system

Where connection is being made to an existing twin walled chimney system and the new and existing chimney systems are of different manufacturer, then an approved adaptor should be used to connect the two chimney systems together.

Complete renewal of the chimney system

If gas operatives have any doubts regarding the existing chimney system's operation or compliance with current standards, or if they suspect its poor condition, the complete chimney system should be renewed (see Essential Gas Safety – Domestic – Part 13 for further guidance).

Chimney system – room-sealed

Free-standing/wall mounted

Replacing free-standing or wall-mounted room-sealed warm air heaters can sometimes be a simple operation, especially when replacing an appliance in the same position. It may only be necessary to make good the building structure internally and externally to suit the new terminal assembly. However, it is important that the terminal is sited correctly (see **Part 11 General installation details – Warm air systems – Natural draught room-sealed warm air heaters** and **Fanned draught room-sealed warm air heaters**.) See also Essential Gas Safety – Domestic – Part 13 for further guidance.

Alternative locations may necessitate major alterations, especially to the warm air ductwork system and return air path. When only slight alterations are necessary, a room-sealed appliance may be more suitable. For example, an open-flued wall mounted warm air heater fitted understairs can sometimes be replaced with a room-sealed down flow model. It may be necessary to adapt the warm air plenum to suit the new heater (see **Warm air plenum** in this Part).

Se-duct/U-duct

When replacing Se-duct and U-duct warm air heaters, the new spigots may not match up with the existing holes. To reduce installation time and to avoid damage to the ducts by re-cutting, warm air heater manufacturers will normally supply a special transfer box manufactured from a corrosion resistant metallic material for a variety of old warm air heater models, complete with detailed installation instructions. These transfer boxes may be offset or right-angled depending on the model (see Figure 10.4) and are supplied in pairs (one each for flue connection and air entry spigots).

Figure 10.4 Transfer boxes

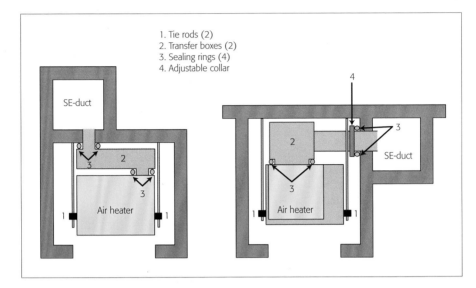

1. Tie rods (2)
2. Transfer boxes (2)
3. Sealing rings (4)
4. Adjustable collar

Figure 10.5 Replacement of a gas, oil or electric brick central heater with a fan-assisted model

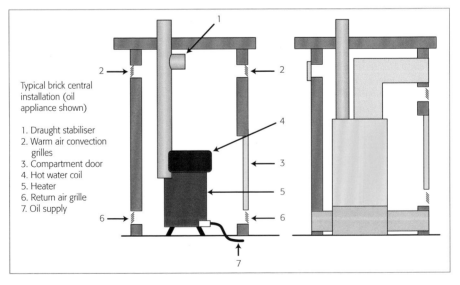

Typical brick central installation (oil appliance shown)

1. Draught stabiliser
2. Warm air convection grilles
3. Compartment door
4. Hot water coil
5. Heater
6. Return air grille
7. Oil supply

Note: Any damage to the building structure should be made good. For more information on Se-duct and U-duct chimney systems (see **Essential Gas Safety – Domestic – Part 13.**

Replacement of natural convection (brick central) models

Type for type replacement

Existing gas, oil fired or electric natural convection 'brick central' model warm air heaters can be replaced using the modern equivalent gas fired appliance.

Fan-assisted type replacement

Where a fan-assisted gas-fired model is specified as a replacement for a natural convection 'brick central' model warm air heater, then the particular appliance manufacturer's instructions should be followed, however, general guidance on this subject is given below (see also Figure 10.5).

Gas fired model

1. Dimensions – ensure that the replacement heater will pass through the compartment door. If not check that structural alterations can be carried out to the door/frame.

2. Compartment – may have to be upgraded to meet current requirements/standards (see **Part 9 Warm air heating – Compartment installations**).

3. Heater Output – where required, allowance should be made for heating additional rooms, for example, bedrooms.

4. Chimney – install a suitable chimney system by either connecting to the existing chimney (if suitable), part renewing or completely renewing (see **Chimney system – open-flue** in this Part). Due to the design of natural convection installations (see **Part 9 Warm air heating – Principle of operation**), the siting will generally be unsuitable for a room-sealed heater.

5. Return air – with a natural convection 'brick central' model warm air heater this type of installation is not normally fitted with a return air system. A positive return air duct and possibly a return air path should therefore be provided (see **Part 9 Warm air heating – Return air (re-circulation)**). Consideration should be given to using an existing high level warm air convection grille for the return air duct connection to the new heater.

6. Compartment/combustion ventilation – is in accordance with the manufacturer's instructions. See also the current British Standard for ventilation requirements: BS 5440-2 for further guidance.

7. Warm air outlets – consider the use of the existing low-level return air openings.

8. Plenum (or base duct) – will need to be provided for the new heater.

9. Ductwork – will be non-existent and may be limited to existing rooms/spaces surrounding the heater. Consider extending the ductwork system to upper floors for example, if the construction of dwelling will permit this.

10. Electrical supply – generally natural convection warm air heaters (other than electrical models) do not have electrical components. Check the availability (see **Part 11 General installation details – Warm air systems – Electrical connections**).

Oil fired model

Existing oil-fired natural convection ('brick central') systems can be replaced following the gas-fired guidance above. However, the existing chimney system requires additional attention:

1. To be acceptable, the chimney system should conform to the requirements of BS 5440-1.

2. Where the existing chimney is known to have given unsatisfactory performance with a previous appliance or fuel, it should be swept and examined. Any faults found should be corrected.

3. Any register plates, restrictor plates or dampers must be removed or permanently secured in the fully open position to leave the main part of the flueway unobstructed.

4. Where necessary, the existing chimney should be lined using a BS EN 1856-2 approved flexible metallic liner.

5. A suitable flue terminal should be fitted.

Note: If gas operatives have any doubts regarding the operation or condition of the existing chimney system it is recommended that it be completely renewed.

Electric model

Existing electric natural convection ('brick central') systems can be replaced following the gas-fired guidance above. However, the additional requirements listed will need to be considered:

1. Gas supply – ensure availability.

2. Chimney – install a suitable chimney system. It may be possible depending on the location, to install a room-sealed warm air heater model.

Replacement of electric fan-assisted models

Where a fan-assisted gas-fired model is specified as a replacement for an existing fan assisted electric warm air heater fitted in a compartment (see Figure 10.6), then the particular appliance manufacturer's instructions should be followed, however, general guidance on this subject is given below:

1. Gas supply – ensure its availability.

2. Dimensions – ensure that the replacement heater will pass through the compartment door. If not check that structural alterations can be carried out to the door/frame.

3. Compartment – may have to be upgraded to meet current requirements/standards (see **Part 9 Warm air heating – Compartment installations**).

4. Heater output – where required, allowance should be made for heating additional rooms, for example, bedrooms.

5. Chimney – install a suitable chimney system (see **Chimney system – open-flue** in this Part).

6. Return air – existing electric fan-assisted heaters, may not have a return air system. Therefore, a positive return air duct and possibly a return air path will need to be provided (see **Part 9 Warm air heating – Return air (re-circulation)**).

7. Compartment/combustion ventilation – is in accordance with the manufacturer's instructions. See also the current British Standard for ventilation requirements: BS 5440-2 for further guidance.

8. Warm air outlets – consider the use of the existing low-level return air openings.

Figure 10.6 Replacement of fan-assisted electric warm air heater

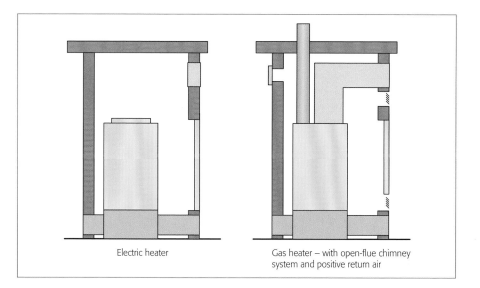

Electric heater

Gas heater – with open-flue chimney system and positive return air

9. Plenum (or base duct) – the existing plenum will need to be adapted to suit the new heater or a new one provided (see **Warm air plenum** in this Part).

10. Ductwork – may be limited to existing rooms/spaces surrounding the heater. Consider extending the ductwork system to upper floors for example, if the construction of dwelling will permit this.

11. Electricity – check suitability (see **Part 11 General installation details – Warm air systems – Electrical connections**).

Return air arrangement

On an existing open-flued warm air heating system, an incorrectly designed or installed return air duct/system, may create a negative pressure within the heater compartment and draw POC down the chimney, through the heater and into the property via the ductwork system, with dire consequences (see Attention). Similar problems can occur when the system is not provided with a positive return air connection or an adequate return air path back to the heater.

A full and unobstructed return air path should be provided to the heater from all heated rooms and spaces, with the exception of kitchens, bathrooms and toilets. This allows air from heated rooms/spaces to be returned to the heater for re-heating and re-circulation. The return air path itself is provided through return air grilles connected by ducts to the heater. Relief air openings allow air to move to the return air grilles from other rooms/spaces but not directly between bedrooms.

Sizing, positions and installation are dealt with in **Part 9 Warm air heating – Return air (re-circulation)**.

Attention: The return air duct/grille arrangement will have been designed for the requirements of the existing heater. Therefore, to ensure the safe operation of the new appliance, the return air arrangement will need to be checked and where necessary upgraded to deal with the requirements of the new appliance in accordance with manufacturer's instructions. Failure to do so could result in an unsafe situation occurring.

Balancing the existing system

Balancing is carried out to ensure that the warm air is discharged to the various rooms/spaces to match their requirements. Balancing should be carried out in accordance with the manufacturer's installation instructions. Reference should be made to the general guidelines in **Part 9 Warm air heating – Balancing the heating system**.

General installation details – Warm air systems – 11

11 – General installation details – Warm air systems

Introduction

The following guidance notes are general to the installation of new and replacement warm air heating appliances and generally apply to fan-assisted model warm air heaters which are the most commonly used type. However, electrical connections, chimneys, gas supply, and ventilation may also be common to natural convection (brick central) models.

Attention: For particular guidance on the installation, commissioning, servicing, and fault finding of circulators (see Gas Installer Manual Series – Domestic – Water heaters).

Warm air heater location

Rooms containing a bath or shower

From 24th November 1984, the Gas Safety (Installation and Use) Regulations require that a gas appliance installed in a room containing a bath or shower must be room-sealed. Prior to this date there were no restrictions and these installations should be classed as Not to Current Standards (NCS) in accordance with the current Gas Industry Unsafe Situations Procedure (see also Essential Gas Safety – Domestic – Parts 8 and 10).

Warm air heaters (room-sealed appliances only) that are installed in locations that contain a bath or shower fall within the scope of BS 7671: 2008 (Requirements for Electrical Installations – IEE Wiring Regulations 17th Edition) and Approved Document P (Electrical Safety) of the Building Regulations (England & Wales).

In these two documents a room containing a bath or shower is classified as a special location due to the increased risks associated with these locations. A person in a bathroom or shower is at greater risk of shock due to a lower body resistance, which could be due to the following:

- lack of clothing, particularly footwear
- presence of water reducing contact resistance
- immersion in water, reducing total body resistance
- ready contact with earthed metal
- increased contact area

Therefore bathrooms have been defined by a zonal concept to indicate the type of electrical equipment which can be used within a particular zone. The zones are made up of three areas, which are:

- Zone 0
- Zone 1
- Zone 2

Note: Additional information can also be found in section 701 of BS 7671.

The zones are determined taking account of walls, doors, fixed partitions, ceilings and floors where these effectively limit the extent of the zone. This means that a zone does not extend through a door opening (with a door) nor does it pass through a fixed partition. However the zone does extend through an opening and around a fixed partition without a door (see Figure 11.1).

Boilers should only be installed in a bathroom if there is no other practical location.

If there is no alternative to installing the boiler in a room containing a bath or shower and it can only be located in one of the zones identified above, then it needs to be suitably rated for use in that particular zone. Suitably rated equipment, including boilers are classified using an International Protection Code (IP).

Figure 11.1 Bathroom zones

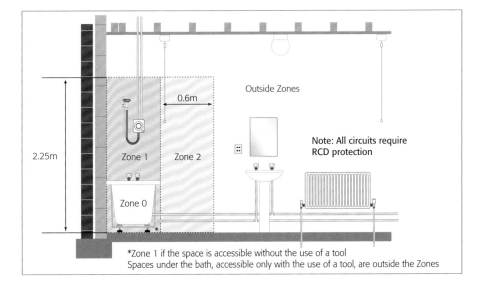

Outside Zones

0.6m

2.25m

Zone 1

Zone 2

Zone 0

Note: All circuits require RCD protection

*Zone 1 if the space is accessible without the use of a tool
Spaces under the bath, accessible only with the use of a tool, are outside the Zones

Table 11.1 IP Ratings

Digit Value	1st Digit (Solids)	2nd Digit (Liquids)
0	No protection	No protection
1	Protected against objects > 50mm	Protected against dripping water
2	Protected against objects > 12mm	Protected against dripping water when tilted ±15°
3	Protected against objects > 2.5mm	Protected against spraying water
4	Protected against objects > 1.0mm	Protected against splashing water from all directions
5	Dust protected	Protected against water jets
6	Dust tight	Protected against heavy seas
7	Not used	Protected against immersion to > 150mm
8	Not used	Protected against submersion to > 1mm
X	Not solid rated	Not liquid rated

Zones 0, 1 and 2 provide a very practical method of specifying requirements for protection against the ingress of water, protection against electric shock, supplementary bonding, etc. in a specific and unambiguous way.

International Protection (IP) Codes

The widely accepted standard IEC 60529 (2001 – 02), which is published by the International Electrotechnical Commission, defines a classification system for the effectiveness of enclosures in preventing the ingress of solids and liquids (see Table 11.1). This system uses two letters – IP (for International Protection) followed by two digits – the first for solids the second for liquids according to the Table 11.1: for example IP 65 implies a dust tight case able to withstand a water jet and is a common level of protection for outdoor equipment.

Zone Scenarios

Zone 1

Question – Can a warm air heater be installed in Zone 1?

Answer – Yes, but the following requirements need to be met:

* the warm air heater cannot be reasonably located elsewhere

* IPX4 (IPX5 Where water jets are likely to be used for cleaning purposes in communal baths or communal showers)

* protected by a 30mA RCD

Question – Can the 230V warm air heater electrical controls be installed in Zone 1?

Answer – No as the controls will not meet the requirements for use in that zone.

Zone 2

Question – Can a warm air heater be installed in Zone 2?

Answer – Yes, but the following requirements need to be met:

* the warm air heater cannot be reasonably located elsewhere

* IPX4 (IPX5 where water jets are likely to be used for cleaning purposes in communal baths or communal showers)

* protected by a 30mA RCD

Question – Can the 230V warm air heater electrical controls be installed in Zone 2?

Answer – No as the controls will not meet the requirements for use in that zone.

Outside Zones

Question – Can a 13Amp socket outlet be installed in a room containing a bath or shower?

Answer – Yes, as long as it is located 3m from the edge of Zone 1.

Question – Is 30mA RCD Protection required?

Answer – Yes, all circuits within a room containing a bath or shower requires RCD protection.

Question – Do I need to fit an RCD to all circuits on an existing installation wired to a previous edition of the wiring regulations in a room containing a bath or shower?

Answer – No, the work you carry out needs to comply with the current requirements of BS 7671: 2008, but you do need to upgrade all of the circuits in that location. Supplementary bonding will be required if there is none present.

Table 11.2 Requirements for equipment in the Zones

Zone	Minimum degree of protection	Current-using equipment	Switchgear and accessories
0	IPX7	Only 12V AC rms or 30V ripple-free DC SELV, the safety source installed outside the zone.	None allowed[1].
1	IPX4 (IPX5 if water jets)	25V AC rms or 60V ripple-free DC SELV or PELV the safety source installed outside zones 0, 1 or 2. The following fixed permanently connected equipment allowed: whirlpool units, electric showers, shower pumps, ventilation equipment, towel rails, water heating appliances, luminaires.	Only 12V AC and 30V DC SELV switches, the source installed outside zones 0, 1 and 2.
2	IPX4[2] (IPX5 if water jets)	Fixed permanently connected equipment allowed. General rules apply.	Only switches and sockets of SELV circuits allowed, the source being outside zones 0, 1 and 2, and shaver supply units complying with BS EN 61558-2-5 if fixed where direct spray is unlikely.
Out of Zones	No requirement	General rules apply.	Accessories allowed and SELV socket-outlets and shaver supply units to BS EN 61558-2-5 allowed. Socket-outlets allowed 3m horizontally from the boundary of zone 1.

[1] The requirements do not apply to switches and controls which are incorporated in fixed current-using equipment suitable for use in that zone or to insulating pull cords or cord operated switches.
[2] The requirement for IPX4 (or IPX5) does not apply to shaver units complying with BS EN 61558-2-5 installed in zone 2 and located where direct spray from showers is unlikely.

Warm air heaters in cupboards within 'Special Locations'

Question – Can a warm air heater (room-sealed appliance only) with a rating of less than IPX4 be installed in a cupboard at the end of the bath or next to a shower tray?

Answer – Yes, if the warm air heater cannot be reasonably located elsewhere then this is acceptable as the zones do not extend into an airing cupboard, providing the cupboard has a door. However, the warm air heater and its controls will need to be out of the reach of the person using the bath/shower.

Also the appliance manufacturer will need to be consulted to see if the warm air heater is suitable for use in a bathroom environment. If the warm air heater is not out of the reach of the person using the bath/shower then it will need to be treated as if it was in Zone 2.

When installing a warm air heater in any of the zones, the whole of the heater must be within the designated zone. If it protrudes into a lower zone the lowest zone criteria must be applied.

Question – Can the controls be located in the cupboard at the end of the bath or next to a shower tray?

Answer – Yes, if the controls cannot be reasonably located elsewhere then this is acceptable, as the zones do not extend into an airing cupboard, providing the cupboard has a door. However the controls will need to be out of the reach of the person using the bath.

Also the control manufacturer will need to be consulted to see if the controls are suitable for use within a bathroom environment. If the controls are not out of the reach of the person using the bath/shower then they will need to be treated as if they were in Zone 2.

Question – Can a warm air heater with a rating of less than IPX4 be installed in Zone 1 or Zone 2 and be boxed in?

Answer – Additional protection can be fitted to cover the warm air heater to give an adequate IP rating providing the manufacturer can confirm this is acceptable.

BS 7671: 2008 states: that every item of equipment shall be of a design appropriate to the situation in which it is to be used or its mode of installation shall take account of the conditions likely to be encountered, including the test requirements of Part 6 of BS 7671.

The warm air heater will also require 30mA RCD Protection if installed in a room containing a bath or shower.

Other requirements

Supplementary Equipotential Bonding may be required to connect together the terminal of the protective conductor of each circuit supplying Class I* and Class II* equipment in Zones 1 and 2 and extraneous-conductive-parts in these zones including the following:

* metallic pipes supplying services and metallic waste pipes (e.g. water, gas)

* metallic central heating pipes and air conditioning systems

* accessible metallic structural parts of the building; (metallic door architraves, window frames and similar parts are not considered to be extraneous-conductive-parts unless they are connected to metallic structural parts of the building)

* metallic baths and metallic shower basins

Supplementary bonding can be omitted if all the following conditions are met –

- main bonding is installed to extraneous-conductive-parts

- all circuits in the room containing a bath or shower are RCD protected by a 30mA RCD

The supplementary equipotential bonding where required may be provided in close proximity to the location, for example:

- an airing cupboard in the bathroom

- an airing cupboard in a location immediately adjoining the bathroom

- in the loft space above the bathroom

If it is not apparent where supplementary equipotential bonding is installed (if required), reference should be made to the location on the Electrical Installation Certificate or Minor Electrical Installation Works Certificate. Also the supplementary bonding clamps need to be accessible.

* Class I equipment – Equipment in which protection against electric shock does not rely on basic insulation only, but which includes means for the connection of exposed-conductive-parts to a protective conductor in the fixed wiring of the installation.

* Class II equipment – Equipment in which protection against electric shock does not rely on basic insulation only, but in which additional safety precautions such as supplementary insulation are provided, there being no provision for the connection of exposed metalwork of the equipment to a protective conductor, and no reliance upon precautions to be taken in the fixed wiring of the installation.

Summary

1. 30mA RCD protection is required on all circuits and equipment in a location containing a bath or shower.

2. Supplementary bonding is not required if RCDs are fitted and main bonding is in place.

3. Electrical equipment must be suitable for use in the location.

Commissioning

It is the responsibility of the gas operative, to ensure that all work has been carried out in accordance with the relevant Regulations and that the gas appliance and installation operate in a safe and satisfactory manner.

When a gas supply is connected to an appliance, there is a requirement in the Gas Safety (Installation and Use) Regulations, that the appliance must be commissioned. Unless this work can be completed immediately the appliance must be disconnected from the gas supply and labelled accordingly.

All gas fittings forming part of the installation must be tested for gas tightness and purged of air (see Essential Gas Safety – Domestic – Parts 6 and 15 for further guidance). Additional information on LPG soundness testing will be found in the Gas Installer Manual Series – Domestic – LPG – Including Permanent Dwellings, Leisure Accommodation Vehicles, Residential Park Homes and Boats.

The warm air heater installation needs to be examined to determine whether a sufficient positive return air path exists from all heated rooms back to the warm air heater 'collection area'. This area will often be the hall or landing of the dwelling. On open-flued appliances, a sealed positive return air duct must connect the return air grille(s) to the return air connection of the heater.

The manufacturer's commissioning instructions supplied with the warm air heater and (where fitted) circulator, must be followed. The following general procedure may be used for appliances covered in this Part. Where a circulator is an integral part of the appliance, commissioning should be carried out in accordance with the manufacturer's instructions. Guidance is also given in the Gas Installer Manual Series – Domestic – Water Heaters.

General procedure

1. Check that the ventilation requirements are correct and in accordance with the manufacturer's instructions (see **Ventilation** in this Part. See also the current British Standard for ventilation requirements: BS 5440-2 for further guidance).

2. Check that the flue termination is correct (see Essential Gas Safety – Domestic – Part 13 for further guidance).

3. Where applicable, carry out a flue flow test (see Essential Gas Safety – Domestic – Part 14 for further guidance).

4. Check electrical connections (see **Electrical connections** in this Part).

5. Test all appliance gas connections with non-corrosive leak detection fluid (LDF).

6. Check that the air filter, air circulation fan and the fan compartment are free of obstructions.

7. Check that the return air and air relief openings are correctly sized and unobstructed.

8. Light the warm air heater in accordance with manufacturer's instructions.

9. Check that the operating pressures, gas rates or both are in accordance with the appliance data plate. Adjust as necessary (see Essential Gas Safety – Domestic – Part 11 for further guidance).

10. Check that all the burners cross light and the flame picture is satisfactory in terms of stability, structure and colour.

11. Check for correct operation of all control valves and that the ignition system (if applicable) operates correctly.

12. If necessary, adjust the pilot flame, to envelop the thermocouple tip. Ensure that it maintains the flame supervision device (FSD) correctly. If the pilot light is extinguished, no attempt should be made to re-light it for 3 minutes.

13. Check the 'fail safe' of the FSD in accordance with the manufacturer's instructions (see Essential Gas Safety – Domestic – Part 12 for further guidance).

14. Following manufacturer's instructions, check that the high limit (or overheat) switch operates correctly by operating the heater with the main burner alight and the fan disconnected. The heater should shut down within 3 to 5 minutes.

15. Carry out a spillage test (see Essential Gas Safety – Domestic – Part 14 for further guidance, also see **Spillage testing** in this Part).

16. Check that the warm air heater thermostats and air temperature thermostat are operating satisfactorily. Depending on the type fitted, turn to the lowest setting, or 'off' position. The warm air heater should go off.

17. Ensure that all diffusers/register shutters open and close freely.

18. Check the warm air heater operation for undue noise arising from mechanical defects or faulty installation such as loose electrical connections, and loose motor or fan mountings.

19. Ensure that any compartment warning labels are correctly fixed (see Essential Gas Safety – Domestic – Part 10 for further guidance).

20. Instruct the user on how to operate the appliance and controls.

21. Where appropriate, instruct the user on the need to clean the air filter regularly.

22. Leave all instructions with the user.

23. Advise the user that the warm air heater will require servicing/safety checks at a minimum of 12 monthly intervals or at intervals specified in the manufacturer's instructions.

24. Advise the user of any appliance/installation defects in writing. If necessary, the current Gas Industry Unsafe Situations Procedure should be followed (see also Essential Gas Safety – Domestic – Parts 8 and 10 for further guidance).

Note: A gas appliance in normal use will require servicing and safety checking at 12 monthly intervals. This period is dependent on the amount of use and the type of room or space it is installed in. It may, therefore, require servicing at intervals less than 12 months.

Spillage testing

A spillage test(s) must be carried out in accordance with the manufacturer's instructions to ensure that the warm air heater chimney system is operating safely. The test(s) should also prove, that suction (negative pressure) created by the air circulation fan on the return air arrangement, does not create a sub-atmospheric pressure in the room/compartment, that can cause spillage of the POC, from the warm air heater and/or circulator (where fitted).

Checks should also be made on any other open-flued appliance (gas, oil or solid fuel) installed in the same or adjoining rooms that may also be affected by the operation of the warm air heater. During the test(s), consideration should be given to the operation of other fans or similar extract devices that are present in the same or adjoining rooms within the dwelling, e.g. cooker hoods, tumble dryers, bathroom/toilet fans, etc.

The appliance manufacturer's spillage test should be carried out with the appliance on and under full operating conditions i.e. outer case on and/or any door to the room or compartment where the warm air heater is installed, closed. During the test the operative should be able to see whether the test is satisfactory or unsatisfactory. However, on some installations the compartment may be so confined that the operative is unable to carryout the test with the compartment door closed.

Under these circumstances the appliance manufacturer should be consulted for a suitable test procedure applicable to their appliance. In the absence of any procedure the test should be carried out on a 'best endeavour' basis, which may require the spillage test to be carried out with the compartment door open.

Where the appliance manufacturer gives no particular guidance, the following advice, may be followed:

Where the draught diverter is accessible – carry out a spillage test following the procedure given in Essential Gas Safety – Domestic – Part 14.

Where the draught diverter is not accessible – (e.g. 'slot-fix'/storey height heaters):

1. Pre-heat the appliance to normal operating temperature.

2. Extinguish the main and pilot burners (ensure the air circulation fan is running whilst carrying out the spillage test, where necessary the 'summer' fan control can be used to ensure the fan is operating).

3. Introduce smoke by means of an ignited smoke pellet on a non-combustible support, into the combustion chamber area of the heat exchanger (see Note).

4. Ensure that there is no spillage evident by visually observing the general area of the down draught diverter on the warm air heater.

5. If spillage is evident, further investigation and remedial work is required before re-testing the appliance.

Gas operatives are reminded that where any doubt exists regarding the safe use of the appliance, the current Gas Industry Unsafe Situations Procedure should be followed (see also Essential Gas Safety – Domestic – Parts 8 and 10 for further guidance).

Note: It is important to ensure that the size of the smoke pellet used will not be too great in relation to the amount of smoke it will produce. In the case of an open-flued appliance, the smoke produced may be greater in volume than the heat exchanger and chimney of the appliance can handle causing smoke to 'spill' from the burner or down draught diverter positions giving a false result. Once the smoke has 'spilt' into the area surrounding the appliance it will make it difficult to detect whether or not there was any spillage in the first place.

Flue testing with decorative recirculatory ceiling fans present

When carrying out a spillage test on an open-flue warm air heater (and circulator where fitted), where there is a re-circulatory ceiling fan fitted in the same room, spillage tests must be carried out with the fan both on and off, at all speeds and where appropriate with the fan operating in each direction.

Tests have indicated that these fans can disturb air movement in the room to the extent that they can cause spillage to occur where none was present with the fan in the 'off' position.

Gas operatives are reminded that where any doubt exists regarding the safe use of the appliance, the current Gas Industry Unsafe Situations Procedure should be followed (see also Essential Gas Safety – Domestic – Parts 8 and 10 for further guidance).

Servicing

It is important to service a warm air heater correctly to maintain the performance of the appliance and to provide the user with optimum comfort conditions. Complaints of lack of performance, which in some cases may influence the user to replace the heater, simply stem from a poorly serviced circulation fan unit impeller and motor assembly being restricted with dust/lint etc.

The manufacturer's instructions supplied with the appliance where available should be followed. They will be specific to the individual appliance. They will recommend intervals of time between services and will include instructions on how to access various components within that appliance. Where a circulator is an integral part of the appliance, servicing should be carried out in accordance with the manufacturer's instructions or where they are not available, guidance is given in the Gas Installer Manual Series – Domestic – Water Heaters.

General procedure (for all appliances when applicable)

The manufacturer's servicing procedure should always be followed. In the absence of instructions, the following general procedure may be used for appliances covered in this part.

Preliminary examination

1. Check with the customer to ascertain any problems with the appliance and/or heating system.

2. Check the location of the appliance is suitable (see **Part 9 Warm air heating – Restricted locations**).

3. Check for any damage that exists on the appliance and surroundings and advise the customer where appropriate before starting any work.

4. Check the operation of the appliance, controls, including thermostats, ignition system, flame supervision devices.

5. Check the appliance burner flame picture(s).

6. Where applicable, check electrical installation complies with the Requirements for Electrical Installations (IEE Wiring Regulations – BS 7671).

7. Check clearances from combustible materials e.g. compartments etc.

8. Check gas installation pipework for exposure to corrosion, sleeving and contact with electrical cables.

Full service

1. Isolate the appliance from the gas supply and where applicable, the electricity supply (see **Electrical connections** in this Part).

2. Because of the possibility of stray electrical currents, consideration should be given to attaching a temporary continuity bond to gas supply and appliance (see Essential Gas Safety – Domestic – Part 5 for further guidance).

3. Remove the main burner – wherever possible the burner should be dismantled and any internal filter or lint arrester gauze cleaned as follows:

   a) All surface dust should be removed using a paint brush or similar.

   b) Using a combination of brushes, remove dust and lint from within the primary air ports, venturi and burner(s).

   c) Check the burner(s) for cracks and metal fatigue.

4. Clean main burner injector(s).

5. Remove the pilot assembly – clean the burner and injector.

6. Check the pilot supply tube is clean and unobstructed.

7. Where necessary, access the heat exchanger and thoroughly clean it using a suitable flue brush or tool.

8. Inspect the condition of the heat exchanger and flueways for signs of metal fatigue (cracking or distortion) (see Attention and **Testing heat exchangers** in this Part).

9. Re-assemble the burner(s) and pilot assembly.

10. Check the condition of the ignition lead and the alignment of the electrode.

11. Turn on the gas and test all disturbed joints for gas tightness using non-corrosive leak detection fluid (LDF).

12. Carefully remove the fan assembly (which generally includes the fan motor) and thoroughly clean the fan blades taking care not to disturb any balance weights (where fitted).

13. Reassemble and refit the fan assembly and where applicable check and refit the fan belt.

14. Restore the electrical supply.

15. If necessary, adjust the pilot flame, to envelop the thermocouple tip. If the pilot flame is extinguished, no attempt should be made to re-light the appliance for at least 3 minutes.

16. Test the flame supervision device (FSD) (or atmosphere sensing device (ASD) where fitted) for correct operation (see Attention and also Essential Gas Safety – Domestic – Part 12 for further guidance).

17. Re-light and check the appliance gas pressure, gas rate or both (where necessary) in accordance with the appliance data plate and adjust as necessary.

18. Check the main burner and pilot for satisfactory flame picture and ensure that they are not disturbed when the air circulation fan is running (see Attention) (see also **Testing heat exchangers** in this Part).

19. Check that the high limit (or overheat) thermostat switch operates correctly by running the heater with the main burner alight and the fan disconnected. The heater should shut down within 3 to 5 minutes (this should be carried out following the manufacturer's instructions).

20. Check that the heater air filter is clean and unobstructed and renew as necessary (see **Part 9 Warm air heating – Air Filters for warm air heaters**).

21. Check the ventilation requirements are correct (see **Ventilation** in this Part. See also the current British Standard for ventilation requirements: BS 5440-2 for further guidance).

22. Where applicable, carry out a flue flow test and check that the flue termination is correct (see Essential Gas Safety – Domestic Parts 13 and 14 for further guidance).

23. Where applicable, carry out a spillage test (see **Commissioning – Spillage testing** in this Part). See also Essential Gas Safety – Domestic – Parts 13 and 14 for further guidance (see Note).

24. Where applicable, check that the room-sealed terminal is installed correctly (a terminal guard should be fitted where necessary) and that no undergrowth will interfere with combustion and adversely affect chimney performance.

25. If room-sealed, check that the appliance case seals are in good condition, renewing any sealing material as necessary. Also ensure that the case itself fits securely and that all fixing bolts/screws are located correctly.

26. Inspect all the return air paths and if the appliance is open-flued, check whether there is a positive return air connection to the appliance (see Attention) (see also **Part 9 Warm air heating – Return air (re-circulation)**) for further guidance.

27. Advise the user to have the appliance(s) serviced/safety checked at a minimum of 12 monthly intervals, or at intervals specified in the manufacturer's instructions.

28. Advise the user of any appliance/installation defects in writing and where necessary, the current Gas Industry Unsafe Situations Procedure should be followed (see Essential Gas Safety – Domestic – Parts 8 and 10 for further guidance).

Attention: Where gas appliances are fitted with an atmosphere sensing device (ASD) pilot, these devices should be serviced in strict accordance with the manufacturer's instructions. They are not 'field adjustable'. This means that if a fault develops on, for example, the thermocouple lead, then it may be necessary to replace the entire unit.

Some manufacturers recommend replacing the ASD every five years (see Essential Gas Safety – Domestic – Part 12 for further guidance).

Attention: Close examination of the heat exchanger is required. Should a crack develop in the heat exchanger, circulation air may be blown into the heat exchanger causing flame turbulence, particularly when the fan switches on (see Testing heat exchangers in this Part).

Flame turbulence can often occur because the heater is not properly sited or sealed onto the plenum, allowing air to escape into the heater compartment. A build-up of pressure can then cause flame turbulence similar to that caused by a heat exchanger fault. If flames are disturbed, further investigation of the heat exchanger condition and/or position and sealing of the heater onto the plenum should be carried out.

Attention: With regard to existing installations, where there is no positive return air connection, the installation should be classed as At Risk (AR) in line with the current Gas Industry Unsafe Situations Procedure (see also Essential Gas Safety – Domestic – Parts 8 and 10 for further guidance).

Where however, there is no provision on the appliance to install a positive return air connection, then advice should be sought from the appliance manufacturer, or other warm air specialist.

Note: Where any room or premises is fitted with a fan (e.g. decorative recirculatory ceiling fan, extract fan, or a fan incorporated within an appliance (including warm air heaters and tumble dryers)), operation of the fan(s) should not adversely affect the performance of the chimney when the appliance is tested in accordance with the manufacturer's instructions (see Essential Gas Safety – Domestic – Part 14 for further guidance).

Note: Whilst there are no specific instructions for servicing a multifunctional gas control valve, gas operatives should be aware that when depressing the pilot control knob to establish the pilot flame, the control knob should be free and easy to operate. Where this is not the case the plastic knob should be removed and a small amount of the control manufacturer's lubricating oil should be applied to the spindle. Failure to correct this fault could lead to a serious gas escape on the control.

Cleaning heat exchangers

Some warm air heater heat exchangers have flueways that are difficult to reach and clean. It is important therefore when servicing such appliances, particularly if the heat exchanger is full of soot, that all flueways are clean. Where soot has accumulated and cannot be removed, it may be necessary to remove the heat exchanger from the appliance to adequately clean it.

Failure to effectively clean these flueways will restrict or prevent the POC from passing through the heat exchanger, which will almost certainly result in the heater becoming blocked with soot once again. During this period the user may be in danger from carbon monoxide poisoning, especially from open-flued appliances.

Testing heat exchangers

Because of the possibility of cracking/leakage occurring, with the prospect of POC entering the property that could contain carbon monoxide (CO), the integrity of the warm air heater heat exchanger should be checked when the appliance is being serviced.

In the absence of manufacturer's instructions, the following test methods may be used.

Method 1

1. Isolate the gas and electrical supplies to the appliance.

2. Where possible, remove the front panel(s).

3. Remove the controls and burner assemblies.

4. Disconnect and remove the air circulation fan assembly.

5. With the aid of a powerful torch, through the fan aperture, examine the heat exchanger externally (looking for cracks and holes) paying particular attention to welded joints. Also check that the chimney is fitted correctly to the top of the heat exchanger.

6. Again with the aid of a powerful torch examine the heat exchanger internally (looking for cracks and holes) paying particular attention to welded joints.

7. With the torch still positioned inside the heat exchanger (being used as a light source), again examine the heat exchanger externally through the fan aperture, in the same places as before, but this time looking for signs of light.

8. Following re-assembly, turn on and re-light the appliance, check and where necessary adjust the burner pressure/gas rate.

9. Visually inspect the flame picture. If the flame picture is disturbed when the warm air circulation fan is running, check for any air leaks between the heater and the plenum, paying particular attention to appliances with a rear down draught diverter. Leakage may also stem from a poorly fitted chimney connection. Rectify any defects/air leaks before continuing with the procedure.

10. Allow the appliance to achieve normal operating temperature (usually 10-15 minutes) and re-check the stability of the burner flame picture making sure that the warm air circulation fan does not affect flame stability.

11. If no defects are found and the appliance is operating correctly, the commissioning/servicing procedure should be completed and the appliance put back into operation.

12. Where defects are found (see Attention).

Method 2

Another test medium that is commonly used to check the integrity of the heat exchanger is the smoke pellet (see Note).

1. The appliance should be lit and allowed to heat up to normal operating temperature (generally 10-15 minutes).

2. Turn off the appliance (gas and electricity).

3. Place a lighted smoke pellet into the combustion chamber (towards the rear) and allow it to burn out.

4. Close all system registers except the one closest to the appliance.

5. Switch on the appliance circulation fan and check for traces of smoke.

6. Where smoke is encountered, the integrity of the heat exchanger and chimney should be checked again visually (see Attention).

7. If no defects are found the appliance should be put back into operation.

8. Turn on and re-light the appliance, check and where necessary adjust the burner pressure/gas rate.

9. Visually inspect the flame picture. If the flame picture is disturbed when the warm air circulation fan is running, check for any air leaks between the heater and the plenum, paying particular attention to appliances with a rear down draught diverter. Leakage may also stem from a poorly fitted chimney connection. Rectify any defects/air leaks before continuing with the procedure.

10. Allow the appliance to achieve normal operating temperature (usually 10-15 minutes) and re-check the stability of the burner flame picture making sure that the warm air circulation fan does not affect flame stability.

11. If no defects are found and the appliance is operating correctly, the commissioning/servicing procedure should be completed and the appliance put back into operation.

12. Where defects are found (see Attention).

Attention: Which ever method is chosen, where the heat exchanger of the appliance is found to be perforated, this should be regarded as Immediately Dangerous (ID) and the current Gas Industry Unsafe Situations Procedure should be followed (see also Essential Gas Safety – Domestic Parts 8 and 10 for further guidance).

Note: Method 2 has its limitations. It is important to ensure that the size of the smoke pellet used will not be too great in relation to the amount of smoke it will produce. In the case of an open-flued appliance, the smoke produced may be greater in volume than the heat exchanger and chimney of the appliance can handle causing smoke to 'spill' from the burner or down draught diverter positions giving a false result. Once the smoke has 'spilt' into the area surrounding the appliance it will make it difficult to detect whether or not there were any leaks within the heat exchanger in the first place.

With method 2, it is also recommended that a visual inspection be carried out on the heat exchanger to confirm its integrity, especially in the area of the combustion chamber.

Maintenance

Where any maintenance work is carried out on a gas appliance e.g. clearing a blocked pilot jet etc. there is a requirement in the Gas Safety (Installation and Use) Regulations that requires an operative to examine:

1. The effectiveness of any flue.

2. The supply of combustion air.

3. Its operating pressure or heat input or, where necessary, both.

4. Its operation so as to ensure its safe functioning.

And forthwith take all reasonable practicable steps to notify any defect to the responsible person and where different, the owner of the premises in which the appliance is situated or, where neither is reasonably practicable, in the case of an appliance supplied with Liquefied Petroleum Gas (LPG), the supplier of the gas to the appliance, or, in any case, the transporter.

Fault finding

Fault finding should always be carried out in a methodical manner. The operation of appliance, burners, control taps, ignition systems, thermostatic controls and flame supervision devices are covered in detail in the appropriate parts of the Essential Gas Safety – Domestic – Parts 1-17. However, the following list helps to apply a methodical approach to fault finding.

General fault finding guide

1. Check with the customer to ascertain what particular problems they have been experiencing with the appliance. This will help to pin point any defects.

2. Check the location and general installation requirements for the appliance are in accordance with the manufacturer's installation instructions.

3. Where possible, always refer to the appliance manufacturer's installation/maintenance instructions as they often contain fault finding information including flow charts to guide the operative to a satisfactory conclusion. They may also contain specific information regarding the testing of and replacement of particular parts.

If an electrical fault occurs after the installation of the warm air heater, a preliminary electrical system check should be carried out by a competent person. On completion of any fault finding task which has required the breaking and remaking of electrical connections, checks should be carried out for continuity, polarity and resistance to earth, of these connections.

Care should be taken during the replacement and handling of electrical components. It is not practical to rectify faults in some assemblies except in the factory and any attempt to do so may render any guarantee or factory replacement void.

Note: Many faults occur on electrical components. It is important that gas operatives are competent to carry out these checks. The fault finding charts (Tables 11.3 and 11.4) only cover basic checks to be carried out. A more comprehensive fault finding chart may be available in the appliance manufacturer's instructions.

Odd coloured gas flames

Some warm air heating appliances covered by this Part, have burner flames that are visible and are exposed to the air in the dwelling. This generally, does not present a problem. However, if a householder suffers with a respiratory condition and uses a Nebulizer to relieve the symptoms, gas operatives should be aware that the gases given off by the respiratory device may affect the flame characteristics and hue. This may, depending upon the concentration of these gases in the room, cause the burner flames to change colour. The colour range may vary from a pale pink to a bright orange. The flames can also appear to be much larger than normal, as salts in the gases expose the full outer mantle of the flame, which is normally not visible to the naked eye.

The flames will return to their normal characteristic size and colour once the room(s) affected by the gas from the Nebulizer have been purged with fresh air.

Electrical connections

General

All Electrical work should comply with the Electricity at Work Regulations.

Electrical connections to the appliance should conform to the Requirements for Electrical Installations (IEE Wiring Regulations) BS 7671.

It is the responsibility, of gas operatives to ensure that all electrical work is carried out by a competent person e.g. operatives approved by the National Inspection Council for Electrical Installation Contractors (NICEIC).

In the case of a warm air heating appliance installation or where installation wiring is routed between the combustion chamber and outer casing, attention is drawn to the higher ambient temperatures that may exist in the enclosure or casing. Care should be taken to ensure that electrical wiring is not subject to temperatures in excess of that for which it is rated.

Electrical isolation

Electrical isolation should be provided so that all voltage can be effectively 'cut off' to prevent or remove danger whilst undertaking any work on the appliance. It should also provide an effective, easily operated means of disconnection and be sited to prevent danger.

The electrical supply point should be installed in a readily accessible position, as close as practical, and within easy reach of the appliance (usually 1.5m) and connected in accordance with the manufacturer's installation instructions with regard to, correct method and polarity, fuse rating, earth connection and voltage range.

Where the electrical isolating point is to be provided for an external installation it should be a waterproof means of isolation.

Table 11.3 Fault finding chart – basic model

Sympton	Possible cause	Action
Pilot will not light.	1. No gas to appliance. 2. Gas supply pipe not purged. 3. Pilot injector restricted. 4. Faulty electrode or cable. 5. Faulty igniter.	1. Check main gas supply. 2. Purge. See Essential Gas Safety – Domestic – Part 15 for guidance. 3. Carefully clear injector or replace. 4. Replace. 5. Replace.

Pilot light goes out on releasing 'Start' button during initial light up or after normal operation.	1. Connection between thermocouple and
	   gas valve loose.
	2. Faulty power unit on gas valve.
	3. Faulty thermocouple.
	4. Pilot flame does not envelop
	   thermocouple.
		1. Check connection and secure.
		
		2. Replace.
		3. Replace.
		4. Adjust as necessary.

Pilot lit but main burner not igniting.	1. Mains electric supply not connected
	   to heater.
	2. Fuse failed.
	
	3. Controls not calling for heat.
	
	4. Loose connection on room thermostat,
	   limit control, gas valve, time control or
	   transformer.
	5. Transformer open circuit.
	
	6. Gas control solenoid operator faulty.
	7. Gas control regulator faulty.
	8. Limit control faulty.
	
	9. Faulty room thermostat or
	   external wiring.
	10. Heater controls set on 'summer'
	    setting.
		1. Check main electrical supply.
		
		2. Replace. If fault occurs again, check
		   room thermostat leads for short to earth
		   with electrical test meter.
		3. Check time control and/or room
		   thermostat is calling for heat.
		4. Check connections.
		
		5. Check with electrical test meter,
		   replace if necessary.
		6. Replace.
		7. Replace.
		8. Check with electrical test meter,
		   replace if necessary.
		9. Check with electrical test meter,
		   replace if necessary.
		10. Reset controls.

Main burner lights but fan fails to run after pre-heat period.	1. Loose electrical connection on fan control. 2. Fan switch settings incorrect. 3. Fan switch faulty. 4. Faulty fan assembly. 5. Burner pressure setting incorrect. 6. Fan belt (if fitted) faulty.	1. Check connections. 2. Check settings. 3. Replace. 4. Replace. 5. Check setting and adjust. 6. Adjust or replace.

Table 11.3 Fault finding chart – basic model (continued)

Sympton	Possible cause	Action
Main burner operating intermittently with fan running.	1. Gas rate or burner setting pressure too high. 2. Temperature rise excessive. 3. Air filter or return air path restricted. 4. Most outlets (registers/diffusers) closed.	1. Check settings and adjust. 2. Adjust fan speed. 3. Check filter is clean and path is clear. 4. Open additional outlets (registers/diffusers).
Fan operating intermittently with main burner lit.	1. Gas rate or burner setting pressure too low. 2. Fan switch setting incorrect.	1. Check settings and adjust. 2. Check setting.
Fan runs for excessive period or operates intermittently after main burner shuts down.	1. Fan switch setting incorrect.	1. Check settings.
Noisy operation.	1. Gas pressure too high. 2. Noisy fan motor/unit. 3. Fan speed setting too high.	1. Check burner setting pressure. 2. Clean fan blades. If still noisy, check the condition of the fan/motor mountings/bearings/alignment of the belt/pulley. Where necessary, replace fan motor/unit. 3. Adjust fan speed.
Main burner remains ON with controls set to OFF.	1. Multifunctional gas valve fails to close down.	1. Disconnect or turn off electrical supply to valve. If burner does not close down, replace valve.

Table 11.4 Fault finding chart – Even Temperature (ET) models only

Sympton	Possible cause	Action
Main burner not lighting, but pilot is alight, voltage detected across gas control valve.	1. Gas pressure regulator set too low. 2. Multifunctional control solenoid operator faulty.	1. Adjust regulator. 2. Replace operator.

Main burner not lighting but pilot alight, voltage **not** detected across gas control valve.	1. Fault in mains electrical supply.
	2. Internal fuse blown.
	3. Replacement fuse blows due to fault in gas control solenoid operator.
	
	4. Replacement fuse blows due to fault in electronic panel.
	5. Fault in external wiring to thermistastat, either:
	  a) Break in circuit.
	
	  b) Reversed polarity.
	
	6. Faulty thermistastat.
	7. Faulty limit control.
	
	8. Faulty electronic panel.
		1. Check electrical supply.
		2. Replace fuse.
		3. Disconnect wires to gas control and check with electrical test meter, check connections and replace solenoid operator if necessary.
		4. Replace electronic panel.
		5.
		
		  a) Check for continuity by bridging at thermistastat plug. Main burner should light.
		  b) Check for correct polarity at thermistastat terminal block.
		6. Replace thermistastat.
		7. Check with electrical test meter, check connections and replace limit control if necessary.
		8. Replace electronic panel.

Main burner lights but fan fails to run even when override switch is set to continuous.	1. Poor electrical connections on fan circuit. 2. Faulty fan assembly. 3. Faulty electronic panel and/or fan speed regulator.	1. Check connections, especially plug and socket. 2. Replace fan assembly. 3. Replace electronic panel and/or fan speed regulator.
Main burner lights but fan fails to run when override switch is set to AUTO from CONTINUOUS.	1. Faulty electronic panel or fan speed regulator. 2. Faulty air flow sensor.	1. Replace electronic panel and/or fan speed regulator. 2. Bridge across airflow sensor. If fan runs replace sensor.

Main burner operates for short periods only on initial light up.	1. Fault in external wiring to thermistastat, either:
	  a) Break in circuit.
	
	  b) Reversed polarity.
		1.
		
		  a) Check for continuity by bridging wires at thermistastat plug.
		  b) Check for correct polarity.

Main burner remains ON with controls set to OFF.	1. Multifunctional gas valve fails to close down.	1. Disconnect or turn off electrical supply to valve. If burner does not close down, replace valve.

The method of connection should provide electrical isolation using either:

1. A fused, double pole switch or spur box; or

2. A fused three-pin plug and a shuttered socket-outlet (except in bathrooms).

Note: In the case of 2, the electrical plug should be removed when servicing the appliance. To encourage this, an unswitched socket outlet is recommended.

Whichever method of electrical isolation is used it should enable an operative to carry out work on the appliance safely.

Operative's responsibility

Before commencing work on an appliance or an installation, the gas operative should ensure that it is completely isolated from the electrical supply. To ensure this an approved test method should be used. In addition, operatives should be confident that the supply cannot be restored without their knowledge in one of the following ways:

1. Where a fused double pole switch, or spur box is fitted – the fuse carrier should be withdrawn, the fuse removed and a small padlock fitted to the carrier in the open position; or

2. Where a plug and socket outlet is fitted – removal of the plug from the socket.

These methods are suitable where the isolation is 'local' and within sight of the operative.

When the isolation is 'remote' a suitable warning notice should be attached to the means of isolation stating – 'Danger Do Not Switch On'. As a precaution where a plug and socket is used, it is recommended that the fuse be removed from the plug for safety.

Note: Further advice on electrical work, is given in the approved Code of Practice for the Electricity at Work Regulations.

Protective equipotential bonding (cross-bonding)

Any person who connects any installation pipework to a primary meter should, in any case where equipotential bonding may be necessary, inform the responsible person that such bonding should be carried out by a competent person.

The Gas Safety (Installation and Use) Regulations places an obligation on gas operatives who install a section of pipework which connects the primary meter or emergency control valve, whether or not the meter or control are fitted, to inform the responsible person of the possible need for protective equipotential bonding where such a requirement did not exist before the work was undertaken and that such bonding should be carried out by a competent person (see **Electrical connections – General** in this Part). The advice should be in writing and the relevant CORGI Services Limited report form (see Essential Gas Safety – Domestic Part 10) may, be used for this purpose.

Although the regulation applies only when new systems are installed and existing ones modified, similar action needs to be taken if a gas operative notices an apparent defect in bonding in other circumstances, e.g. during maintenance checks (this applies to both protective or supplementary equipotential bonding).

In addition to protective equipotential bonding supplementary bonding of pipework may be necessary in locations of increased risk of electrical shock, e.g. bathrooms and shower rooms. In such cases, a competent electrical engineer should be consulted.

The positioning of protective equipotential bonding where fitted to internal and external gas meter installations are shown in Essential Gas Safety – Domestic – Part 5.

Chimneys

Open-flues

Only chimneys and chimney fittings complying with BS EN 1856-1 should be used. The chimney installation should be installed in accordance with the manufacturer's installation instructions. Guidance on the installation of chimneys and termination positions will be found in Essential Gas Safety – Domestic Part 13.

Before installing a warm air heating appliance to an existing chimney system the correct operation of the chimney should be verified by carrying out a flue flow test. On completion of the installation, a spillage test should be carried out in accordance with the manufacturer's instructions to ensure that the POC are being safely removed (see also Essential Gas Safety – Domestic Part 14 for further guidance and **Commissioning** in this Part).

A chimney previously used for an appliance burning a fuel other than gas should be swept thoroughly before installing any gas appliance.

Note: The installation of combined warm air heaters/circulators to open-flues, should be carried out in accordance with manufacturer's instructions.

Poured/pumped concrete chimney liners

These are acceptable alternatives to flexible metallic liners, but should only be carried out by a competent contractor. Poured/pumped concrete chimney linings should be installed by a method that has been certificated by an accredited test house. Always check to ensure that the lining is mechanically sound before installing any appliance. Chimneys with this type of lining that have been used with another fuel should be swept and carefully examined before use with a gas appliance.

Flue terminals

Where a brick/masonry chimney has been lined with a rigid metal chimney system or flexible metallic liner, or where an appliance has a direct flue connection, an approved terminal should be fitted (see Essential Gas Safety – Domestic – Part 13 for further guidance).

A chimney of 170mm diameter or less across the axis of its outlet should be fitted with a terminal. The size of the terminal should not be less than the nominal size of the appliance flue connection (see Essential Gas Safety – Domestic – Part 13 for further guidance).

Flue testing

When planning the installation of an open-flue warm air heating appliance to an existing chimney system its correct operation should be verified (see also Essential Gas Safety – Domestic – Part 14 for further guidance).

On completion of the installation and commissioning process the appliance and chimney should be tested in accordance with the manufacturer's instructions to ensure that POC are not spilling into the room (see Essential Gas Safety – Domestic – Part 14 for further guidance). However, some warm air appliance manufacturers have spillage testing instructions specific to a particular model. Where this is the case the information will be found in their installation instructions (see also **Commissioning – Spillage testing** in this Part).

Natural draught room-sealed warm air heaters

Choosing the terminal position on the outside wall is probably the most critical part of the installation.

For gas to burn correctly (complete combustion) POC should readily disperse and pass freely away from the concentric flue terminal (combined air inlet and flue outlet duct) into the atmosphere and not mix with clean fresh air passing through the air inlet duct to the burner.

Little sympathy can be expected, should the gas operative install a heater to harmonise with kitchen units only for the flue outlet position to be restricted by an adjacent projection outside e.g. buttresses, gate posts, soil pipes, internal or external corners of buildings etc. These are known as 're-entrant' positions i.e. the POC are prevented from being blown away by the wind but re-circulate around the flue terminal and may 're-enter' the appliance via the fresh air inlet duct.

The POC vitiate this fresh air and reduce the oxygen content.

Consequently, this has a profound effect on combustion quality of the burners and is likely (depending on the degree of vitiation) to cause the flames, including the pilot flame, to become ragged and lift off the burner. In the case of the pilot burner, this could eventually lead to cooling of the thermocouple, which in turn could cause the appliance to fail to safety.

The condition is particularly aggravated on windy days (see Essential Gas Safety – Domestic – Part 13 for further guidance).

In the examples given, the condition may be regarded as unsafe. If found by a gas operative, the current Gas Industry Unsafe Situations Procedure should be followed (see also Essential Gas Safety – Domestic – Parts 8 and 10).

Conditions similar to those described above will also be experienced if the concentric flue and air inlet duct is cut too short for the wall thickness. In this situation, the air inlet grilles are likely to be obstructed or blocked by cement mortar, which restricts air entrainment and adversely affects the combustion process.

Other 're-entrant' positions are openings into buildings such as doors, windows and ventilators.

Some appliance manufacturers now stipulate particular dimensions where flues should be sited away from openings into buildings and these should always be complied with. In the absence of particular instructions, the operative should seek guidance from the appliance manufacturer.

It is also important that the terminal is positioned so that the POC can safely disperse at all times e.g. when the termination is into a car-port or other similar structure, there should be at least two open unobstructed sides to that structure. Attention to the material used on the roof and allowance for adequate clearances/protection of the roof should be provided.

Terminals should not be sited into a passageway, pathway or over adjoining property where they can be a nuisance or cause injury (see Essential Gas Safety – Domestic – Part 13 for further guidance).

Some natural draught room-sealed warm air heaters are also suitable for installation onto 'Se-duct' or 'U-duct' chimney systems.

Fanned draught room-sealed warm air heaters

Installation requirements are generally the same as those for natural draught room-sealed heaters, although the siting of a terminal for a fanned draught warm air heater is not so critical. This is because the fan assists with dispersal of the POC, thereby eliminating most of the problems associated with the siting of natural draught room-sealed terminals.

Whilst the siting requirements are more relaxed, the same precautions as for natural draught room-sealed flue terminations need to be taken, e.g. when the termination is close to openings into buildings or is into a car-port or other similar structure.

Care should also be taken to ensure that the POC and any pluming are not blown onto an adjacent property, causing a nuisance (see Essential Gas Safety – Domestic – Part 13 for further guidance).

These warm air heaters are generally designed to incorporate several flueing options with side, rear or vertical flue outlet positions available.

Gas supply

The Gas Safety (Installation and Use) Regulations require operatives installing gas installation pipework and fittings, to ensure that they are installed safely. They must give due regard to the position of other pipes, pipe supports, drains, sewers, cable, conduits and electrical apparatus and to any parts of the structure of any premises in which it is installed, which might affect its safe use.

After connecting the appliance, the installation must be tested for gas tightness and all installation pipes through which gas can flow must be purged of air (see Essential Gas Safety – Domestic – Parts 6 and 15 for further guidance). Additional information on LPG soundness testing will be found in the Gas Installer Manual Series – Domestic – LPG – Including Permanent Dwellings, Leisure Accommodation Vehicles, Residential Park Homes and Boats.

Note: Guidance on the installation of pipework/fittings and pipe sizing can be found in Essential Gas Safety – Domestic – Part 5.

Ventilation

General

All open-flue gas appliances need air for combustion and to assist the safe operation of the chimney.

Gas appliances up to 7kW heat input (gross or net) generally do not require ventilation to be provided but rely for their correct operation and that of the chimney on adventitious ventilation to the room.

Guidance on ventilation, adventitious ventilation, compartment ventilation etc. and the installation of ventilation grilles and sizes will be found in the current British Standard for ventilation requirements: BS 5440-2.

Warm air heaters supplied with combustion air from a ventilated roof space

In today's modern, air tight constructed dwellings which often include draught and sound proofing material, an alternative method of providing air for combustion is by drawing air from the roof space into the warm air ducting system. This method eliminates the need for openings in walls, doors or windows and reduces the risk of draughts.

Depending on the appliance manufacturer's particular requirements, the construction of the dwelling and the position of the warm air heater it may be advantageous to use the following fan assisted method of introducing air for combustion.

1. Connect a duct (fitted with a bird guard) from a ventilated roof space, or from a waterproof grille on an outside wall, to the return air duct or return air plenum on the warm air heater (see Figure 11.2).

2. A lockable damper should be installed in the fresh air duct and adjusted to provide the necessary volume of air. A minimum airflow rate of $2.2m^3$ per hour should be drawn into the air chamber for every 1kW of the appliance maximum input rating (net). The gas operative should carry out this adjustment. Following completion of the commissioning procedure, the damper should be locked in position to prevent adjustment by unqualified persons.

3. When the heater operates, its fan will draw in external air, mix it with the return air and circulate it throughout the warm air distribution ducts. Warm air should be circulated into the room/space where the heater is installed using a non-closing register fitted in that area.

Note: Where this method of air supply is used, reference should be made to the appliance manufacturer's installation instructions for further guidance.

Figure 11.2 Fanned air supply

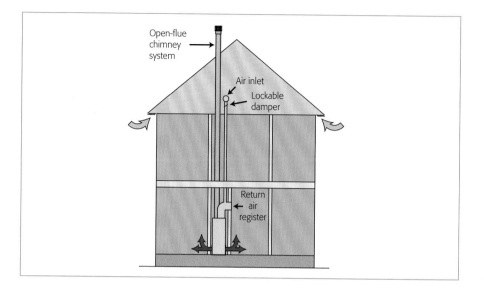

General appliance details – 12

Controls particular to warm air heaters

Room thermostat

For basic fan assisted models a 24-volt room thermostat is essential to ensure close control and comfort conditions. A heat anticipator is located within the thermostat and is graded in amps. The heat anticipator should be checked and where necessary adjusted to correspond with the amp rating of the multifunctional gas valve (normally set to 0.2 amps).

The room thermostat will bring on the main burner when it is calling for heat provided that any time control is set to an 'on' period. The thermostat controls the warm air system output from the air temperature it senses. Selection of its optimum location is most important.

Two main choices of location are:

1. In the living room, where the temperature has the most significant effect on comfort; or

2. Close to the main return air grille. This position is preferable for systems that are likely to be used continuously to heat all rooms.

The thermostat should be mounted:

1. For buildings of one or two storeys high, at a height of 1200mm to 1500mm above floor level.

2. For buildings over two storeys in height, it should be mounted in the living room at a height between 1370mm and 1830mm above floor level. Its maximum setting should not exceed 27°C.

3. On an inside wall.

4. Away from direct sunlight and other local heat sources, e.g. space heating appliances, wall light fittings or television sets.

5. Away from warm air ducts, diffusers, registers or the heater itself.

6. Away from outside walls, doors, or windows.

On modern warm air heating systems, the room thermostat and the programmer control the main gas valve. The fan is controlled by a series of other controls.

Overheat control

If air is not circulating through the heat exchanger of a warm air heater it can quickly become overheated. Therefore, there is a requirement for an electronic cut-off device to shut off the gas supply to the main burner to prevent overheating occurring. The maximum temperature is set at 110°C.

To prevent overheating, an overheat or a limit thermostat (see **Limit thermostat** in this Part) or in some cases both can be used. The overheat is usually provided, as an additional control for down-flow heaters because, in these models, the filter assembly at the top of the heater can quickly rise to a high temperature if the fan assembly is slow in switching on.

Limit thermostat

This is similar to the overheat control and on many warm air heaters is the only temperature limiting device fitted. The limiting temperature is set at a maximum 95°C. The bimetal-switching device is wired in series with the gas control valve. The limit thermostat has a differential setting of about 15°C. So the heater will be turned on again when the temperature falls to about 80°C. Because the limit thermostat is automatically reset, the heater will cycle on and off every few minutes when an overheat condition occurs.

Fan switch

If the fan and the gas control valve were both switched on at the same time, (as was the case with many old warm air heaters in the past), the fan would start to blow cold air into the rooms before the heat exchanger had time to heat up.

To prevent this, modern heaters are fitted with a thermally operated switch, which delays the operation of the fan until the heat exchanger has reached a pre-determined temperature. It is normally operated by a bimetal-switching device located in the outlet of the heat exchanger and is wired in series with the fan.

Usual temperature settings are:

- fan 'off' at about 38°C
- fan 'on' at about 58°C or
- 'differential' of about 20°C

The operation of the fan switch will switch on the fan when the air in the heat exchanger has reached about 58°C. When the gas solenoid has closed, the fan will continue running until the temperature of the air leaving the heat exchanger has fallen to about 38°C. This ensures that the residual heat from the appliance is fully utilised.

Fan delay unit

Another type of fan switch is a 'fan delay unit' which consists of a micro-switch operated by a bimetal strip which is heated by a resistor. The resistor is in series with the room thermostat, in the low voltage circuit and the micro switch is in the 230V AC supply to the fan.

When the programmer is switched on and the room thermostat is calling for heat the gas control valve becomes energised and the fan delay unit resistor begins to heat up. After about 90 seconds, the bimetal strip operates the micro-switch and switches on the fan.

When the room reaches the required temperature, the room thermostat switches off and the supply to the resistor is cut off. The fan then continues to run for a short period while the resistor cools down.

Summer/winter switch

This is a simple, manually controlled switch, fitted in the main voltage supply to the fan. If the user wishes to run the fan in the summer to circulate cool air through the rooms (when the heating unit is not operating), the switch is changed to the 'summer' position.

Even temperature (ET) controls

Fan assisted warm air heaters with basic controls are generally operated by a 24 volt thermostat, which when calling for heat, operates an electrical panel which brings the main burner on at a pre-selected gas rate. The fan switch will then bring on the air circulation fan at a single pre-selected speed.

Warm air will be circulated and delivered through the ductwork system until the room thermostat is satisfied, when the heater will simply shut down.

Generally, draughts and noise can be a problem on short ducted systems, and there may be a significant temperature difference across rooms/spaces.

Some manufacturers have overcome this problem by designing modulating gas burners and/or air circulation fans to give more even temperature control.

They are operated by an electronic controller called a 'Thermistastat', (fitted instead of a room thermostat), which is a heat sensitive resistor sending a continuous signal to the heater (it should be located as for a **Room thermostat**).

The thermistastat senses the heat requirements and continuously sends signals of varying strengths to the electronic controls in the heater to control the rate of warm air delivery. The warm air heater controls automatically adjust the operation of both the gas burner and the air circulation fan. The main burner cycles at approximately 2 minute intervals and the fan speed is then matched to the heater output.

Definitions

1st family gas: at present normally only LPG-air.

2nd family gas: Natural gases.

3rd family gas: Liquefied Petroleum Gases (LPG).

Access plate: a removable plate giving access into a combustion chamber and/or heat exchanger.

Adventitious ventilation: ventilation obtained through gaps around doors, floors and windows, for example.

Aerated burner: a burner in which some or all of the required air has been mixed with the gas before it leaves the burner port(s).

Air heater: appliance for heating air to be used for space heating.

Air vent free area: total area of the unobstructed openings of an air vent.

Air vent: non-adjustable grille or duct, which allows the passage of air at all times.

Anemometer: instrument for recording wind speed.

Annular space: space between a flexible metallic flue liner and brick/masonry chimney.

Appliance (gas): appliance designed for heating, lighting, cooking or other purposes.

Appliance compartment: an enclosure (not being a habitable space) specifically designed or adapted to house one or more gas appliances (see also **Balanced compartment** in this Part).

Appliance ventilation duct: provided to convey combustion or cooling air for an appliance or component.

Atmosphere sensing device: (also known as an oxygen depletion system) shuts off the gas supply to an appliance burner before there is a build up of a dangerous quantity of products of combustion in the room concerned.

Background central heating: simultaneous space heating to temperatures below those specified for full central heating.

Balanced compartment: method of installing an open-flued (Type B) appliance as room-sealed, so that flueing and ventilation provide a balanced flued effect.

Balanced flued appliance: a room-sealed appliance (Type C) which draws its combustion air from a point adjacent to that at which the products of combustion are discharged, the inlet and outlet being so disposed that wind effects are substantially balanced.

Basement (LPG appliances): a room, which is completely or partly below ground level on all or some sides.

Bedsitting room: any room or space used for living and sleeping purposes.

Boiler: appliance designed to heat water for space heating and/or water supply.

Boot: a transition from the round or rectangular duct to the diffuser/register.

Bottled gas: normally Butane or Propane stored as a liquid under pressure in refillable portable containers.

Branched flue system: a shared open-flued system serving appliances situated on two or more floors.

Bulk storage vessel: permanently installed vessel of approved design for the storage of LPG under pressure, which is filled on site.

Calorific Value (or CV): the Calorific Value is the quantity of heat (energy) produced when a unit volume of the fuel, measured under standard conditions of temperature and pressure, is burned completely in excess air.

A distinction is made between:

a) Gross Calorific Value – (also known as the Higher Calorific Value or HCV) – in the determination of which the water vapour produced by the combustion of the fuel is deemed to have been condensed into a liquid phase at the standard temperature and its latent heat released.

b) Net Calorific Value – (also known as the Lower Calorific Value or LCV) – in the determination of which water vapour produced by the combustion of the fuel is assumed to remain in the vapour phase. The net Calorific Value is therefore the gross Calorific Value minus the latent heat of the water vapour contained in the combustion products.

Capacity (of a gas meter): maximum rate that gas will flow through the meter, measured in m^3/hr or ft^3/hr.

Central heating system: a fixed system for warming a building from a single source of heat, with manual or automatic control of the operation of the whole system and of the temperatures in the heated space.

Chimney liner: pipe inside a brick/masonry chimney to form a flue. May be rigid or flexible.

Chimney pot: prefabricated unit fitted at the outlet of a chimney.

Chimney system: a complete assembly of chimney components from one or more appliances to a single terminal, including primary flue(s) and draught diverter(s), if any.

Circulation pipe: pipe forming part of the primary circuit of a hot water system.

Circulator: boiler with a rated heat input not exceeding 8kW (gross), designed primarily for the supply of domestic hot water in conjunction with a separate storage vessel.

Cistern: a fixed container for holding water at atmospheric pressure.

Cold feed pipe: the pipe from the feed and expansion cistern to the water heating system.

Collection area: where all heated rooms/spaces are connected to one area by means of a number of air relief openings.

Combination hot water storage unit:

1) a hot water supply apparatus comprising of a hot water storage vessel with a cold water feed cistern immediately above it, the two being fabricated together as a compact unit.

2) a hot water supply apparatus comprising a hot water storage vessel with a cold water feed cistern beside it or inside it.

Commissioning: initial start-up of an installation to check and adjust for safe and reliable operation.

Competence: competence in safe gas installation requires gas operatives to have enough knowledge, practical skill and experience to carry out the job in hand safely, with due regard to good working practice. Knowledge must be kept up-to-date with awareness of changes in law, technology and safe working practice.

Condensate drain: a device in a flue where condensate can be removed.

Condensing appliance: designed to use latent heat from water vapour in the combustion products by condensing the water vapour within the appliance.

Damper: a device used to vary the volume of air passing through a confined cross-section by varying the effective cross sectional area.

Data plate: a durable, permanently fixed plate bearing specified information relative to the appliance.

Designed heat loss: the heat loss from a building estimated from considerations of the structure and the intended working temperature(s) and ventilation rates.

Dew point: the temperature of a mixture of combustion products and water vapour at which further cooling results in condensation of the water vapour.

Diffuser: a fitment equipped with a damper or moveable louvers that permit adjustment or closure of an opening from which air discharges. Generally fitted in a floor or ceiling.

Direct hot water storage vessel: storage vessel with no internal heat exchanger, heated directly by an appliance containing the same water.

Double-feed indirect hot water storage vessel: any indirect hot water storage vessel that requires a separate feed cistern to both the primary and the secondary circuit.

Draught brake: an opening into any part of an open-flue chimney system, including that part integral with the appliance.

Draught diverter: prevents interference to the combustion of an open-flued appliance; must be fitted to the manufacturer's instructions and in the same room, space or compartment as the appliance, with at least 600mm of vertical chimney above it.

Draw-off point: hot water taps.

Drop-out time: time taken for the flame supervision system to respond to a loss of flame.

Ducted warm air heater: flued appliance, which uses ducts to distribute the heated air.

Emergency control valve (ECV): valve for shutting off the supply of gas in an emergency; not a service isolation valve (see also **Additional emergency control valve (AECV)** in this Part).

Enforcing authority: an authority with a responsibility for enforcing the Health and Safety at Work Etc. Act 1974 and other relevant statutory provisions; normally Health and Safety Executive (HSE) or the local authority for the area as determined by the Health and Safety (Enforcing Authority) Regulations 1977.

Equipotential bonding (electrical cross bonding): electrical conductor between a point close to the outlet of a gas meter and the earth terminal (such bonding does NOT involve connecting electrical power to gas pipework).

Fanned draught flue system: flue system in which the draught to remove products of combustion is produced by a fan.

Fanned draught room-sealed appliance: an appliance that, when in operation, has the combustion system including the air inlet and the products of combustion outlet, isolated from the room or space in which the appliance is installed. The draught to operate the flue is created by an integral fan.

Feed and expansion tank: cistern which supplies cold water to the primary circuit of a heating system which allows the expansion of the system water when hot.

Fire compartment: room or space constructed to prevent the spread of fire.

Fire stop: a barrier or seal of non-combustible material that is designed to prevent or retard the passage of smoke or flames.

Flame failure: the loss of a flame from the normally detected position.

Flame retention: prevention of flame-lift off.

Flame supervision device: control, which detects the presence of a flame and in the absence of that flame, prevents the uncontrolled release of gas to the burner.

Float (ball) – operated valve: a valve for controlling the flow of water into a cistern.

Flow pipe: a pipe in a primary hot water circuit in which water moves away from a circulator.

Flue break: an opening in the secondary flue in the same room as and in addition to, the opening at the draught diverter.

Flue outlet: the part of the appliance that allows the exit of products of combustion from the appliance.

Flue safety device: a device designed to detect adverse flue conditions (down draught) at the appliance draught diverter; also known as a TTB.

Flue terminal guard: fitted to prevent human contact (especially that of children) with a terminal and to prevent interference with the terminal or damage to it.

Flue terminal: device fitted at the flue outlet to:

1. Assist the escape of products of combustion.

2. Minimise downdraught.

3. Prevent flue blockages.

Flue termination: the outlet of a chimney system where products of combustion discharge into external air.

Flue: passage for conveying the products of combustion from a gas appliance safely to atmosphere.

Free area: total area of the individual unobstructed openings of an air vent.

Gas fittings: "Gas fittings" means gas pipework, valves (other than emergency controls), regulators and meters and fittings, apparatus and appliances, designed for use by consumers of gas for heating, lighting and other purposes, for which gas can be used (other than the purpose of an industrial process carried out on industrial premises), but it does not mean:

1. any part of a service pipe.

2. any part of a distribution main or other pipe upstream of the service pipe.

3. a gas storage vessel.

4. a gas cylinder or cartridge designed to be disposed of when empty.

Gas meter: an instrument for measuring and recording the volume of gas that passes through it without interrupting the flow of gas.

Gas Safety Regulations: legally binding requirements for safe gas work.

Indirect hot water storage vessel: any hot water storage vessel in which the stored hot water is heated by the primary heater through which hot water is circulated from a circulator without mixing of the primary or secondary water taking place.

Individual chimney system: chimney system, which serves a single appliance only.

Insulated chimney – factory-made: complete assembly of all essential factory-made insulated sections, fittings and accessories to convey the products of combustion to the outside air.

Latent heat of condensation: the quantity of heat removed, at constant temperature during the change from the gaseous to liquid state.

Latent heat: the quantity of heat (energy) added to or removed from, a substance at constant temperature during a change of state.

Lint arrester: a fibre pad or metallic mesh designed to trap a mixture of dust, fluff, fibres and droplets of grease which would otherwise collect in the airways of a burner.

Liquefied Petroleum Gas (LPG): normally commercial Propane or Butane gas, stored in a vessel under pressure, which turns into a liquid state.

Lock-out: a safety shut-down condition of a control system such that restart cannot be accomplished without manual intervention.

Main flame: flame on the main burner.

Manometer: instrument(s) for the measurement of gas pressure. Includes 'U' and electronic gauges.

Manufacturer's instructions: documents supplied with the gas appliance/equipment by the manufacturer giving guidance on how to use, service, maintain and install the product.

Mechanical ventilation: air supplied by a fan.

Meter regulator: a device located in close proximity and upstream of a primary meter which is used solely to control the pressure of the gas within the gas installation.

Non-combustible material: that which has passed tests for non-combustibility in accordance with British Standards.

Open vent pipe: a pipe connected to an open water system communicating with the atmosphere.

Open-flue chimney system: system that is open to a room or internal space at each appliance.

Open-flued appliance: an appliance designed to be connected to an open-flue chimney system which draws combustion air from the room or space in which it is installed.

Oxygen depletion system: shuts off the gas supply to an appliance burner before there is a build up of a dangerous quantity of products of combustion in the room concerned, also known as an atmosphere sensing device.

Pluming: visible cloud of products of combustion from an outside flue terminal, which are cooled to below dew point by mixing with external air.

Pre-aerated burner: a burner to which gas and air are supplied already mixed.

Pressure gauge: instrument for indicating or recording pressure.

Pressure regulator: automatically maintains a constant outlet pressure.

Pressure test point: small plug type fitting on a meter, installation pipe or appliance, allowing attachment of a pressure gauge.

Primary circuit: a circuit in which water circulates between a circulator and a hot water storage vessel.

Protected shaft: a shaft which enables persons, air or objects to pass from one compartment to another, enclosed within a fire-resisting construction.

Protected stairway: a stairway including an exit passageway leading to its final exit, enclosed within a fire-resisting construction (other than any part that is an external wall of a building).

Register plate: a fire-resistant plate used to seal the annular space around the base of a flexible metallic flue liner and brick/masonry chimney (see **Annular space** in this Part).

Register: a fitment equipped with a damper or moveable louvers that permit adjustment or closure of an opening from which air discharges. Generally fitted in a wall.

'R' type adaptor: see Ridge terminal adaptor ('R' type adaptor) in this Part.

Responsible person: the occupier of the premises or, where there is no occupier or the occupier is away, the owner of the premises or any person with authority to take appropriate action in relation to any gas fitting therein.

Return air duct: a duct through which air returns to a warm air heater.

Return pipe: a pipe in a primary hot water circuit in which water moves back to a circulator.

RIDDOR: The Reporting of Injuries, Diseases and Dangerous Occurrences Regulations 1995.

Ridge terminal adaptor ('R' type adaptor): a fitting for connecting a circular cross-sectional pipe to the rectangular-section connection of a ridge flue terminal.

Ridge terminal: a terminal designed for fitting at the ridge of a building.

Room-sealed: an appliance that, when in operation, has the combustion system, including the air inlet and the products outlet, isolated from the room or space in which the appliance is installed.

Safety shut-off valve (SSOV): actuated by the safety control so as to admit and stop gas flow automatically.

Secondary flue: the part of the open-flued system connecting a draught diverter or draught break to the terminal.

Se-duct: a duct serving special room-sealed appliances; it is open at both ends and rises vertically in buildings to bring combustion air in and take products of combustion out.

Sensible heat: the quantity of heat added to, or removed from a substance during the finite temperature change.

Single-feed indirect hot water storage vessel: an indirect hot water storage vessel, which has only one cold feed pipe connection to supply both the primary and secondary circuits.

Sleeve: duct, tube or pipe embedded in the building structure allowing the gas installation pipework to pass through a wall or floor; capable of containing the gas.

Temporary continuity bond: a means of providing electrical continuity on a gas supply for safety reasons.

Thermistastat: thermostat containing a thermistor – containing a semiconductor device having a resistance that decreases rapidly with an increase in temperature – used for temperature control.

Thermostat: a thermally actuated control device for maintaining a desired temperature.

Through-room: any room formed by the removal of an intercommunicating wall between two rooms, or any large room formed by two open plan smaller rooms. The opening/archway present between two smaller rooms may have sliding or intercommunicating doors.

Tightness test: the testing of installation pipes and equipment for escapes from the system.

Transfer grille: non-adjustable fitment in a wall, door, or partition, to transfer air between adjacent rooms and/or spaces.

Transporter: a person other than a supplier, who conveys gas through a distribution main.

U-duct: literally, a u-shaped flue system; combustion air is provided by one limb and special room-sealed appliances are connected to the other. The U-duct ends are open and adjacent.

Valve: device to stop or regulate the flow of gas by the closure or partial closure of an orifice by means of a gate, flap or disc.

Vented hot water storage system: a water storage system that is open to the atmosphere via an open vent pipe.

Ventilation opening: includes any means of ventilation, which opens directly to external air, such as the openable parts of a window, a louvre, airbrick, progressively openable ventilator or window trickle ventilator. It also includes any door, which opens directly to external air.

Ventilation: the process of supplying fresh air to and removing used air from, a room or internal space.

Warning pipe: an overflow pipe so fixed that its outlet, whether inside or outside a building, is in a conspicuous position where the discharge of any water from it can be easily seen.

Work: in relation to a gas fitting this includes any of the following activities carried out by any person, whether an employee or not:

a) Installing or reconnecting the fitting.

b) Maintaining, servicing, disconnecting, permanently adjusting, repairing, altering or renewing the fitting or purging it of air or gas.

c) Where the fitting is not readily movable, changing its position; and

d) Removing the fitting.

Note: work in this context does not include the connection or disconnection of a bayonet fitting or other self-sealing connector.

CORGI Services Limited publications – 14

14 – CORGI Services Limited publications

Gas – Domestic

Manual Series

GID1	Essential Gas Safety
GID2	Gas Cookers and Ranges
GID3	Gas Fires and Space Heaters
GID4	Laundry, Leisure and Refrigerators
GID5	Water Heaters
GID6	Gas Meters
GID7	Central Heating – Wet and Dry
GID8	Gas Installations in Timber/Light Steel Frame Buildings
GID9	LPG – Including Permanent Dwellings, Leisure Accommodation Vehicles, Residential Park Homes and Boats
GID11	Using Portable Electronic Combustion Gas Analysers for Investigating Reports of Fumes
GID12	Using Portable Electronic Combustion Gas Analyers – Servicing and Maintenance
FFG2	Fault Finding – wet central heating systems Domestic

Pocket Series

USP1	The Gas Industry Unsafe Situations Procedure
SRB1	Ventilation Slide Rule
GRB1	Gas Rating Slide Rule Natural Gas – Domestic
TTP1	Tightness Testing and Purging
FFG1	Fault Finding Guide
TTG1	Terminals and Terminations

Learning Aids

TWB1	Gas Safety Domestic (CCN1) Workbook
TWB2	Domestic gas-fired central heating/hot water boilers and circulators up to 70kW (CEN1) Workbook
TWB3	Domestic gas-fired cooking appliances (CKR1) Workbook
TWB4	Domestic gas fires and wall heaters (HTR1) Workbook
TWB5	Domestic gas water heating appliances (WAT1) Workbook
TWB7	Domestic combustion performance analysis on gas-fired appliances (CPA1) Workbook
ACS3	CORGI ACSelerate – Core Natural gas
ACSMOD2	CORGI ACSelerate – Gas-fired central heating – Wet
ACSMOD3	CORGI ACSelerate – Flueless domestic gas cookers
ACSMOD4	CORGI ACSelerate – Flued domestic gas cooker ranges
ACSMOD5	CORGI ACSelerate – Gas fires and space heaters
ACSMOD6	CORGI ACSelerate – Gas-fired Water Heating (Domestic)
ACSMOD7	CORGI ACSelerate – Gas-fired central heating – Dry
ACSLPG	CORGI ACSelerate – Core Liquefied Petroleum Gas

Design Guide

WAH1   Warm Air Heating System
             Design Guide

Forms

CP1   Gas Safety Record

CP2   Leisure Industry Landlord's Gas
             Safety Record

CP3FORM Chimney/Flue/Fireplace and Hearth
             Commissioning Record

CP4   Gas Safety Inspection

CP6   Service/Maintenance Checklist

CP12   Landlord/Home Owner Gas
             Safety Record

CP14   Warning/Advice Notice

CP21   Condensing Boiler Installation
             Assessment Form

CP25   Maintenance Work Report

CP26   Fumes Investigation Report

CP32   Gas Testing and Purging –
             Domestic (NG)

CP43   Safety Check for existing
             chimney/flue systems in voids

Labels

CP3PLATE Chimney/Hearth Notice Plate

WLID   Immediately Dangerous Warning
             labels/tags

WLAR   At Risk Warning labels/tags

TG5   Tie on Uncommissioned
             Appliance labels

TG8   Void Property Tag

WL5   Gas Emergency Control Valve labels

WL7   Install/Service labels

WL8   Compartment/Ventilation labels

WL9   Electrical Bonding labels

WL13   Serviced By Label

WL15   Flueless Water Heater Label

Gas – Non-Domestic

Manual Series

ND1 Essential Gas Safety Non-domestic

ND2 Commercial Catering and Laundry Non-domestic

ND3 Commercial Heating Non-domestic

Pocket Guide

USP1 The Gas Industry Unsafe Situations Procedure

Learning Aids

TWB6 Gas safety for Non Domestic heating (COCN1) Workbook

TWB9 Gas safety for Non Domestic pipework (COCNPI 1LS, ICPN1, TPN1, TPCP1, TPCP1A and EFJLP1) Workbook

TWB10 Gas safety for Non Domestic catering and appliances (CCCN1 and COMCAT 1-5) Workbook

ACSND CORGI ACSelerate Non Domestic – Core

ACSND2 CORGI ACSelerate Non Domestic – Commercial Laundry

ACSND3 CORGI ACSelerate Non Domestic – Commercial Heating

ACSND4 CORGI ACSelerate Non Domestic – Commercial Catering

ACSND5 CORGI ACSelerate Non Domestic – Liquefied Petroleum Gas Change Over

ACSND6 CORGI ACSelerate Non Domestic – Larger pipework, boosters and tightness testing

Forms

CP15 Plant Commissioning/Servicing Record (Non-domestic)

CP16 Gas Testing and Purging (Non-domestic)

CP17 Gas Installation Safety Report (Non-domestic)

CP42 Gas Safety Inspection (Commercial Catering Appliances)

Labels

WLID Immediately Dangerous Warning labels/tags

WLAR At Risk Warning labels/tags

WL10 Emergency Control Valve labels

WL12 Meter Housing key labels

WL14 Emergency Control Valve Location Tags

Electrical

Manual Series
ES1   Essential Electrical Safety

ITWS1   Inspection and Testing of Domestic Central Heating Wiring Systems

Pocket Guide
CRPB   Electrical Component Exchange Pocket Book

Learning Aid
TWB8   Essential Electrical workbook

Forms
CP22   Minor Electrical Installation Works Certificate

CP23   Domestic Electrical Installation Certificate

CP24   Electrical Safety Warning/Advice Notice

CP27   Domestic Periodic Inspection Report

CP35   Electrical Control Wiring Certificate

CP37   Testing Equipment Check List

Labels
WL16   Electrical Isolation Warning Tag

WL20   WARNING: Disconnection Label

WL25   Electrical Safety Warning/Advice Tag

WL26   Electrical Safety Warning/Advice Label

WL27   Portable Appliance Testing Labels

WL28   Electrical Caution Notice

WL29   Electrical Warning Notice

Plumbing

Manual Series
HEM1   Hygiene Engineering

Pocket Guide
CDP1   Commissioning of Water Pipework – Domestic

Design Guides
WCH1   Wet Central Heating System Design Guide

UVDG   Unvented Hot Water Systems Design Guide

Forms
CP7   Central Heating Survey

CP20   Central Heating Commissioning/Inspection Record

CP33   Commissioning of Water Pipework

CP34   Central Heating Cleansing Record

CP40   Bathroom Quality Check Sheet

CP41   Combined Pressure Test Record Sheet

Labels
TG6   Pressure Test Tag

TG7   Plumbing Warning Tag

Renewables/Energy Efficiency

Manual Series

EEM1	Ground Source Heat Pumps
EEM2	Domestic Solar Hot Water Systems
EEM3	Domestic Biomass Systems

Forms

CP38	Gas Fired Home Heating Installations – Energy Efficiency Checklist
CP39	Commercial heating Installations – Energy Efficiency Checklist

Health and Safety

Manual Series

HS1	Health and Safety Guide
HS5	Health and Safety Task Manual

Forms

HS2	Risk Assessment Record
HS3	Personal Protective Equipment Register

Business

Forms

CP18	Estimate of Works Pad
CP19	Invoice form
CP36	Customer Complaint Record
RP1	RIDDOR (F2508G2) Pad

Labels and Notices

NA1	Sorry We Missed You Cards
NA2	No Tools Kept On This Vehicle Overnight Notice
NA3	No Smoking Label

Notes